THE PATIENT ELEPHANT

Also by David Taylor and published by Robson Books

Vet on the Wild Side

THE PATIENT ELEPHANT

**More exotic cases from the
world's top wildlife vet**

DAVID TAYLOR

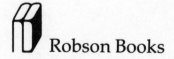

Robson Books

For Christine

First published in Great Britain in 1993 by Robson Books Ltd, Bolsover House, 5–6 Clipstone Street, London W1P 7EB

British Library Cataloguing in Publication Data
A catalogue record for this title is available from the British Library

ISBN 0 86051 835 3

Typeset by Columns Design & Production Services Ltd, Reading
Printed and bound in Great Britain by Hartnolls Ltd, Bodmin, Cornwall

Contents

There is no reason whatever to believe that the order of nature has any greater bias in favour of man than it had in favour of the ichthyosaur or the pterodactyl.

H G Wells

A seagull alighted in a suburb of the capital of Lu. The Marquis of Lu welcomed it and feasted it in a temple hall, ordering the best music and grandest sacrifices for it. But the bird remained in a daze, looking quite wretched, not daring to swallow a morsel of meat or a single cup of wine. And after three days it died.

This was entertaining the seagull as the Marquis of Lu liked to be entertained, not as a seagull likes to be entertained.

Zhuang Zhi, third or fourth century BC

Acknowledgements

My grateful thanks to Krystyna Wojciechowska who so meticulously and cheerfully typed out my manuscript.

And to my good friend Niki Levy.

Introduction

People pursue the things
they like; things
don't change, but people's feelings do;
some say a crane can dance
quite well, but for me,
no dance it does can equal
its grace while standing
silently alone.

Bai Juyi, AD 618–907

Every aspect of my work with animals has changed significantly since I went to treat my first wild animal in 1957; was it a leopard or a Celebes black ape with an upper respiratory infection? I have forgotten. There have been thousands of leopards and black apes, as well as hundreds of other species, from spiders to snakes, gorillas to grizzly bears, pandas to penguins, over the intervening years. The major causes of disease in zoos and wildlife parks back then were parasites and faulty diet. Now we have new, or at least newly recognized, viruses such as the morbillivirus of the seal and dolphin epidemics, 'Mad Cow Disease' and feline Aids in certain big cats and many deadly viruses of primates such as those causing Marburg Disease and Kyasanur Forest Disease which seem to have emerged from the jungles of Africa, Asia and South America.

But there is no doubt that, overall, the health and well-being of zoo animals has improved beyond imagination, at least in the collections of the western world. Techniques for diagnosis and treatment of disease are now highly sophisticated. When I began work as a zoo vet little research was being carried out into the problems of wild animals. Of their basic requirements, their nutritional needs, their reproductive behaviour, we knew little – certainly for ninety-nine per cent of species. Anaesthesia was clumsy and dangerous. Lack of normal values for the physiological parameters severely hampered analysis of blood or other tissue samples. Some drugs that had proved safe and effective in domestic and farm animals caused untoward reactions in exotics. Penicillin and certain other antibiotics, fine for dogs and horses, were found to kill rodents, including hamsters and guinea pigs. Fly sprays safe for use near domestic pets had alarming effects on dolphins and porpoises.

My life after qualifying as a veterinary surgeon has been one of continuous learning, even more of re-learning. The standard veterinary textbooks were of limited use. Anatomical differences abound between *my* patients and the ones on which teaching concentrates at the universities. Elephants have no pleural (chest) cavity. Dolphins have no gall bladder. A snake has one lung that can stretch much of the way down the length of its body.

Physiology is another minefield. The normal temperature of an armadillo, if recorded in a fox terrier, might give you the impression that the poor mutt was suffering from exposure. The normal sweat of the hippopotamus is red – it is *not* blood seeping through the skin.

And then there is behaviour. The wide world of exotic species contains all manner of normal, perhaps surprising, idiosyncrasies. Bushbabies urinating on their hands aren't afflicted with some weird psychological vice or bladder trouble – they are simply wetting the pads of their fingertips (like bank clerks dampening theirs, though not usually by peeing on them, before counting cash!), the better to climb with. Whales lying motionless upside down, blow holes submerged, for many minutes at a time, are basking, not about to shuffle off the mortal coil.

Now there is so much research, so much involvement in

aspects of conservation of endangered species, so many new advances, that if I sat all day and all night, seven days a week, reading the literature flowing from these endeavours I could not absorb all the information. Within the small profession of zoo and wild animal veterinarians, specialization is becoming ever more essential. I began by tackling all creatures great and small (*pace* my colleague Alf White, alias James Herriot) that *weren't* domesticated. Now I have to concentrate on marine mammals and certain other 'special' (to me) animals such as elephants, pandas and the big cats. One of my partners is a world-class exotic-bird specialist, another a specialist wild-animal anaesthetist and otter expert. One of my former assistants for many years has become the authority on problems of gazelles, and another is heavily into fish medicine.

Since 1957 the quality of European and American zoos has risen immeasurably. There are now very few slum menageries remaining. Zoos such as Jersey, San Diego, Frankfurt, Madrid and Kolmarden have led the way in studying and breeding rare animals. The Zoo Act and the Dangerous Wild Animals Act have brought major advances in the welfare of exotic animals in Great Britain, and international conventions are gradually cutting off the disgraceful illegal trading in creatures such as baby gorillas and chimpanzees, endangered parrots and reptiles. The public now *expect* and demand zoos to be places where the emphasis is on conservation, welfare, education and science, not mere museums of living animals or 'gawping boxes', as a keeper in Lancashire once described them. Take Sea World, USA, for example. In the past two years this organization has rescued, rehabilitated and returned to the oceans more marine mammals than it has captured in the past twenty-eight years.

Working abroad as I do for about seventy per cent of my time, I still see some examples of bad zoos, especially in the third world. Recently I was in Angola at the request of the BP oil company to advise on what might possibly be done with the small Luanda Zoo. Conditions in the zoo were sleazy enough – reminiscent to me of British zoos such as Knaresborough and the Brontë Zoo, mercifully closed many years ago. Animals in cramped quarters. Shortage of the correct food stuffs. But then just over the wall of the Luanda Zoo lie thousands of miserable hovels where human beings live in far worse conditions. I was cross, but could hardly complain, when the emaciated soldiers guarding the gates of the zoo stole some of the cakes that a concerned American friend of mine took as treats for the reasonably plump chimpanzees living inside. A lady has just telephoned me to say that Haile Selassie's last remaining lion in a cage in Addis Ababa is looking pretty sick – can I help the creature? I have agreed to go out to Ethiopia – at no fee – if she can make arrangements to gain access to the lion. But with the awesome scale of human suffering in the Horn of Africa being displayed daily before our eyes on television and in newspaper photographs, I do have a twinge of moral anguish over the matter. Much as I love lions.

In 1992 the unthinkable happened. Windsor Safari Park, the finest of its kind in Europe, went into receivership and, unbelievably, could not be sold as a going concern. I have been involved in the Park since it was started by the Smart family in 1968. Windsor without its Safari Park – the hippos in the lake, the dolphinarium where such healthy babies have been born in recent years, the fine herd of young elephants – doesn't bear thinking about. I have such vivid memories of working there. The giraffe Caesarean, the killer whale that swallowed a ball, the first litter of cheetah cubs, the rhinoceros whose horn I had to remove (for medical, *not* Chinese aphrodisiac reasons). Now the site is going to be plastic and utterly devoid of animals as a Legoland. But at least I am a member of the expert committee advising the receivers on the dispersal of the stock. There will be *no* euthanasia, *no* dealing with circuses, animal trainers or laboratories, *no* splitting up of established social groups, *no* sending animals to places with facilities that are not at least as good as those at Windsor. It won't be easy and we've only got a year to complete the operation. Already certain unsavoury characters are coming out of the woodwork, trying to get their hands on some or all of the six-hundred-odd animals. The zoological world is relatively small – we know the black sheep, and they will succeed only over my dead body.

Tomorrow afternoon I fly to Croatia to inspect the quarters for polar bears at Zagreb Zoo. Things, as I said, have changed immensely for me as a zoo vet during the years since that black ape or leopard or whatever it was. But I still have a fierce love for my profession, and hope to die with my boots (surgical white ones) on. The changes that have occurred, for good or ill, I welcome with open arms, for as Confucius said, 'They must often change who would be constant in happiness or wisdom.'

1

The Patient Elephant

The' unwieldy elephant,
To make them mirth, us'd all
    his might and wreathed
His lithe proboscis.

Milton, *Paradise Lost*, Book iv

The elephant keeper had at first thought that Ellie was for some reason developing the habit of breaking wind whenever he was around and had taken to addressing her as 'Ellifart' except when the director was present. After hearing the loud flatulent sound on and off for some days, he finally tracked down its source, not to Ellie's rear end, but to somewhere at the opposite pole of her three-ton body. Ellie was blowing raspberries and the keeper got the impression that she waited until his back was turned before emitting a noise more commonly associated with red-nosed clowns and pantomime dames than middle-aged and well-mannered Indian elephants. He was wrong about that. The windy trump was indeed intermittent but unintentional, and far from enjoying the man's discomfiture when he turned to brush the floor or fetch more hay and heard a rude 'praaaaa' behind him, Ellie herself was getting fed up with it. Her trunk didn't seem to belong to her any more.

Elephants have always been particularly special patients of mine. The first zoological drama I ever witnessed as a student seeing practice at Belle Vue Zoo in Manchester in 1951 was the autopsy of an old elephant, all of its joints ravaged by osteoarthritis, at one time a major scourge of the species and still something I dread finding when one of them goes lame. It was at Belle Vue that I had extracted my first elephant molar during an operation that had lasted many hours, and then lost my patient to waterlogging of the lungs because the safe and reversible modern anaesthetics for such beasts had not yet been invented. There were so many others ... The elephant with a tumour the size of a rugby ball that I'd excised successfully in an Italian circus, the elephant in Norfolk with an apple stuck in its throat, the elephant in Germany whose blood I had drawn off into an ozone-generating machine for 'washing' and then returned to its owner's circulatory system. I'll never forget the eight-year-old elephant cow in Arabia with chronic heart disease whose life had been mightily improved by the digitalis contained in dried foxgloves which were fed to her daily mixed with lucerne. Hundreds of cases of chiropody on overgrown or under-run toenails, needing the application of my Black and Decker sanding machine and socks made of sacking soaked in formalin to kill foot rot fungus. Baby elephants with hernias repaired by stitching patches of plastic mesh under the belly skin to support the weak muscle around the 'belly-button' or umbilicus. And, of course, tooth troubles. Elephants have a strange dental arrangement of teeth which are always imperceptibly on the move towards the front of the mouth. Consequently they sometimes jam, causing me and other zoo vets all sorts of problems. An elephant with toothache beating its head against a tree or a wall which eventually collapses, is an awesome sight to behold. I've hammered, chiselled, levered and pulled out elephant teeth in little Italian circuses, capital city zoos, and once on the promenade of a Majorcan tourist resort. If it is true that an army marches on its stomach, an elephant marches on its feet and its teeth. Keep those two departments in good condition, and the animal might possibly live to be a hundred.

Ellie, the raspberry-blowing elephant at Flamingo Park Zoo in Yorkshire where I was veterinary officer and assistant director in 1969, was something out of the ordinary. We'd always got on well, right from the first day we met. She had run her trunk tip all over me, rooted around in my pockets and found a strip of chewing gum which, paper and all, she had promptly taken and chewed, purring like a giant-sized cat. That mega-purr is one of my favourite animal sounds, along with the 'prooch-prooch' of tigers who talk to you, and the whistle of killer whales with whom it is also possible to conduct a conversation of similar sounds when travelling with them. All these are magical noises to me. We humans like to be liked by our fellow creatures, particularly wild ones. God knows, we do little enough to deserve any such affection.

Ellie was the matriarch of the elephant herd at Flamingo Park. She kept the boisterous group of young African elephants in order, rewarding good behaviour by handing out a banana or a chunk of bread, picking it up by the prehensile tip of her tongue and popping it directly into the open mouth of the favoured recipient. Bad behaviour was dealt with by a stern trumpeting, a cuffing about the head, delivered again by her trunk, or the sudden drenching of the miscreant's head with a trunkful of cold water. On warm days she was allowed to wander around the zoo's spacious grounds in the company of her keeper, picking flowers and leaves here and there if she fancied a snack, purring over visitors who wanted to meet her, and flinging gravel and sand from the pathways over her back from time to time to discourage flies. She was particularly fond of going to look at the elephant seal, an enormous adult female who lived in a long rectangular pool. There was some sort of affinity between the land elephant and the sea elephant, as elephant seals are sometimes called. Standing with her front feet on the pool edge, Ellie would gently stroke the seal as it swam slowly by. The elephant seal seemed to relish the tickling touch of the elephant's trunk, and never tired of moving to and fro, apparently revelling in this form of light massage. I was with her one afternoon when I witnessed a most unusual occurrence. Another keeper had thrown some herring for the elephant seal while the elephant keeper was giving Ellie a loaf of bread. Ellie dropped the loaf which fell into the pool and was at once gobbled down by the elephant seal. Immediately, Ellie snatched a floating herring from the water, conveyed it to her mouth, chewed it happily and swallowed it. I've written before about the carnivorous appetites of elephants – and hippopotamuses – so perhaps I shouldn't have been so surprised. But an elephant seal eating Hovis?

Bliss for Ellie was the wire brush that hung on a hook in the elephant house. Many skin diseases in elephants arise when they don't have access to pools of water or wallows of mud. Even on my walk with Ian Botham and two elephants over the Alps in 1988 I had arranged that, from time to time, Ian would march the elephants through marsh land where the animals could splash and roll in the dark ooze to their hearts' content. It did their skins a power of good. Ellie had a pool at Flamingo Park, but I still insisted that the keeper scrub her skin twice a week with the wire brush to stop skin scales building up into the leathery patches under which infection can develop and that I have seen in so many elephants in badly run circuses. Elephants may be physically thick skinned (their characters certainly are not), but they are very sensitive to touch, and Ellie utterly adored the scratching of the wire bristles. She would purr and caress the keeper's head of long blond hair with her trunk tip while he groomed her. If she thought a brushing was overdue, she would try to find an opportunity to unhook the brush from the wall and then hand it to the nearest human being. 'Get on with it,' she would purr – or so I imagined.

On hearing the report of the elephantine raspberries, I went to look at Ellie. Sure enough, after a few minutes standing in front of her while she did the routine frisking of my person – elephants would make excellent airport security guards, I suspect – I heard the rude sound. 'Praaa,' it went. There was absolutely no doubt where it was coming from – the trunk. Somewhere about halfway up its length. Ellie looked at me with her moist, dark grey eyes and flapped her ears slowly. Her expression was at once both intelligent and soulful. 'Sorry about that,' she seemed to be saying silently, 'but I can't help it.' 'Praaa,' went her trunk yet again. 'Praaa, praaa, praaa'. I watched the elephant breathing. 'Praaaa'. It happened as she exhaled. A few minutes later, there it was again, on exhalation. Never when she breathed in, sometimes when she breathed out. I put the diaphragm of my stethoscope on to the skin of her trunk. 'Praaa'. It nearly deafened me, and when she inhaled her next breath I heard a faint but brief hissing sound.

'I wonder if she's got a foreign body – a piece of food or a button or a coin up there?' I said to her keeper. 'Something she's somehow sniffed up. I've never had a case but I suppose it *could* happen.' Even now I still see something new every day. Nothing seems to be impossible. After all there was the dolphin at Woburn Dolphinarium that suffocated after some idiot dropped a penny into its blow-hole which was open for a split second when the animal surfaced to take in air. A one-in-a-million chance that turned out to be rapidly fatal. And there was the chimpanzee in Manchester that I'd saved from choking to death after it swallowed a small plastic Mancunian coat-of-arms that it had stolen from the top of an iced cake at an Animals and Owners luncheon. But I'd never heard of a case of an elephant sucking something up its trunk which then got stuck.

Everything else about Ellie seemed completely normal, so I decided to take no action for the present, just wait and see what transpired. From then on the daily report sheet from the elephant section regularly referred to Ellie continuing to make the unusual sound. What was more, the keeper thought it was becoming louder and more frequent. One morning he came to my office in the converted farm cottage at the centre of the zoo. 'Ellie's nose is bleeding,' he announced. 'Just a little trickle coming down the left side of her trunk.'

I went at once to the elephant house. Drops of scarlet fell from Ellie's trunk tip as she conducted the routine search of my pockets. Ulcer? Tumour? I wondered. Something would have to be done, but how? You can't look up five feet of trunk by shining a pen-light into the end.

'Don't give her any food today,' I told the keeper. 'Keep her indoors and sweep away all the straw bedding so she can't eat that. She can drink up until early evening, but no water after then. I'll knock her out tomorrow morning and see if we can find the cause of all this.' Then I went back to my office and telephoned a famous firm of surgical instrument manufacturers in London. I needed to borrow a flexible endoscope, the sort used for looking into human colons for the detection of bowel cancers and the like. These tubes, with an overall diameter no greater than that of my little finger, are up to one and a half metres long and carry their own light source, water and air supply, suction and electrocautery facilities. Ideal for going where I wanted to go – not up a human rectum, but Ellie's trunk. The instrument company, intrigued by my request for help in such an unusual task, readily agreed to the loan of a suitable endoscope and at once sent it to King's Cross, together with an assortment of accessories, in time to be put on board the next train up to York.

Next morning I had an extra thick layer of straw bedding put down in Ellie's quarters and, before the hungry elephant could begin scoffing it, injected her with the then fairly new and remarkably effective anaesthetic, M.99. Five minutes later she sank slowly to her knees at the front end and after another minute did the same with her hind legs. As she lay unconscious, breathing automatically with muscles relaxed, the noise from her trunk on exhalation now accompanied every breath. The airway was being significantly obstructed by something. Normally elephants take in about seventy per cent of the air they need through the trunk, but they can, if necessary, mouth-breathe. I didn't think there was much chance of Ellie asphyxiating while I examined her.

The endoscope was already connected to its light source. I lubricated the length of it with a thin film of local anaesthetic gel, and then very gently introduced the tip into the left 'nostril' of Ellie's trunk. 'Now,' I said to the keeper, 'I want you to feed the instrument slowly into the trunk as I instruct you. When I say "forward", push in. When I say "back" withdraw it. And, of course, stop when I say "stop". If you feel any resistance stop feeding it in and tell me.' I would be busy looking down the eyepiece at the other end of the endoscope and manipulating the controls clustered there. Numbered white rings on the tube would indicate how far up the trunk the tip of the endoscope was at any particular moment.

I began. 'Forward, forward, forward, gentle now,' I said quietly. Elephants under M.99, though unconscious, are very sensitive to loud noises. Through the lens I could see a pink tunnel streaked with a little mucus and blood stretching on into darkness. 'Forward, forward – stop!' The way ahead was blocked by what resembled a glistening pink boulder that almost completely filled the passageway. It was a tumour, and it had all the characteristics of a benign non-cancerous polyp. I tried to slide the endoscope past it to see how far it extended and whether I could get a glimpse of its attachment to the nostril wall, but to no avail. I didn't want to use force and perhaps make it bleed. I pulled back a short distance and watched. As Ellie breathed out the 'boulder' rolled towards me and came to an abrupt halt, restrained by its attachment. The air squeezing past the polyp set up the vibrations we could hear as the 'raspberry'. When the elephant breathed in the polyp moved back up the trunk and came to rest where the nostril was slightly broader and the airflow less restricted. I asked the keeper to push the endoscope in again until it touched the polyp. 'Stop!' I said and, taking my eye from the eyepiece, looked at the measuring marks on the outside of the tube. Forty-five centimetres. The polyp lay at a distance up Ellie's trunk as long as my forearm with fingers outstretched.

I pulled out the instrument and switched off the light. A small injection of antidote into an ear vein and Ellie was on her feet once more within three minutes. 'How are you going to get it out?' asked the elephant keeper. He sounded and looked distraught. Ellie and he were inseparable friends.

'I'll think of something,' I said. 'One thing's for sure, I don't think I can remove it via the nostril. The endoscope can't get past the blockage. And I've no idea how thick its "neck", the stem connecting it to the nostril wall, may be.'

'But you've got to do something, doc.' The Yorkshire lad – supremely gifted at handling elephants, though I doubt whether he'd ever been as far as London let alone Africa or India – had tears in his eyes. 'You've got to.'

'I will,' I replied. 'But it needs careful consideration. I'll see you later.' Ellie blew a raspberry as I walked out of the elephant house. And well she might – I had never tackled anything like this before. What *was* the best way?

I went to my office, brewed some tea, and sat staring out of the window towards the lovely Vale of Pickering. 'How on earth am I going to unpack your trunk, Ellie?' I asked myself. 'Not funny. Not funny at all,' I answered.

There was only one possible approach. Open the trunk over the polyp and cut it out. I'd never done anything like that, nor had anyone else that I knew. The trunk of an elephant is a remarkable structure containing, so folks say, forty thousand muscles and a complex network of blood vessels and nerves. I had seen several elephants with the condition termed 'trunk paralysis', where the proboscis suddenly loses all power and the animal can no longer deliver food or water to its mouth. This paralysis is generally thought to be due to some injury to one of the cranial nerves where it emerges through a hole in the skull below the eye. What if I damaged the nerves lower down by any incision I made, and thus caused what would probably be a permanent paralysis? I'd never come across a detailed anatomical illustration of the nerve network in the elephant trunk. The dissection of noses – of horses, cattle, sheep and dogs – that I'd done seventeen years before in the anatomy room on Glasgow's Buccleuch Street wouldn't be of much help now.

At last I made up my mind. I went back to the elephant house and found the keeper sitting on a hay bale stroking Ellie's trunk and talking to her softly. 'You're going to be right as a clock, luv,' he murmured. 'Right as a clock.' His face was pale and tear-streaked.

'She can feed lightly today and tomorrow,' I said. 'Let her get over the anaesthetic. Then, the day after tomorrow, no food and restrict her water again. I'll operate the day after that, Saturday. We'll begin at seven o'clock in the morning.'

The elephant keeper's face was instantly transformed. His eyes brightened and a faint grin began to form on his lips. 'Oh, thanks, doc, thanks!' He threw up an arm and for a moment I thought he was going to shake my hand. 'That's bloody gradely.'

By the time Saturday morning arrived I had completed the operation a dozen times, step by step, in my mind. Blood vessels lying in unexpected places I could deal with, using forceps and ligatures. Nerves were a different matter. I would try to make no transverse cuts across the trunk to minimize the risk of severing any. All strokes of my scalpel would be lengthways. Blood loss should be insignificant in such a large animal. The anaesthesia with M.99 was well-tested, reliable and safe. I couldn't imagine the actual removal of the polyp taking very long. Obstruction to the airway wasn't a worry with the other nostril and mouth not being involved. At the end of all this armchair surgery I was beginning to feel rather optimistic. Except for the little voice that kept reminding me how often animals had sprung unpleasant surprises on me in the past. Like the wolf that had suffered a stroke after I had done nothing more than inject him with some vitamin B12.

I anaesthetized Ellie in the same way as before and once she was down, 'raspberrying' away, I brought a small table into her loose box and placed it near her head. Covering it with a sterile cloth, I laid out my instruments. Operating on such large animals is always best done in their own quarters – hardly operating theatre conditions, but I have had remarkably few cases of post-operative infection over the years. I scrubbed in a bucket of warm water and iodine disinfectant and prepared the skin of Ellie's trunk by washing it first with Betadine and then with alcohol. Elephant skin is always ingrained with dust and dirt. The keeper sat by Ellie's head, stroking her temples and looking tense. I had calculated where the polyp lay by measuring forty-five centimetres from the tip of the trunk with a steel tape. A single stroke of my scalpel made an incision some four inches long. Blood welled up from a layer of exposed muscles and I began clipping off the bigger blood vessels. That done I cut down through another layer, repeated the haemorrhage control and then split a longitudinal sheet of tissue by spreading open the blades of long pointed scissors jabbed into it. The outer surface of her nostril lining lay pale and gleaming before me. I slit it with care and there was the polyp, an elongated pink tumour with rounded ends. One could have mistaken it for an uncooked pork sausage. I ran my index finger underneath it and found its attachment to the nostril, a short neck about the thickness of a pencil. The next step was to pass a length of catgut round the neck, pull it tight to garrotte it, and then knot the ligature firmly. I snipped through the neck above the knot and withdrew the polyp through the incision. 'What's a Walls' banger doing in there?' I asked, throwing the tumour towards the keeper who caught it with one hand and gazed at it with a big smile on his face. Now it was time to close the wound. I sutured the muscle layers with catgut and finally closed the tough skin with a line of stainless steel wire stitches. Sitting back on my heels, for I had been working kneeling, I noticed for the first time that the raspberry sound of Ellie's breathing was no more. Nothing remained but to puff a sulphonamide fly-deterrent powder over the operation wound, inject Ellie's rump with a large dose of antibiotic and anti-tetanus booster, and then administer the antidote as before.

One of the first signs that the M.99 was being neutralized, a minute after the antidote went into her ear vein, was, to my delight and a great whoop of joy from the keeper, a twitching of Ellie's trunk. It writhed slowly where it lay on the straw like an inebriated python. It wasn't paralysed! Ellie flicked an ear, sighed deeply, turned on to her brisket, brought her hind legs up beneath her belly, and with one mighty heave got to her feet. Still under the influence of the final traces of anaesthetic she looked down at us sleepily. And then put out her trunk and touched her keeper's face as if to show him that there was no need to worry any more.

'I don't want her sucking water up the trunk in order to drink for the next few days,' I said. 'Give it time to heal. You'd better water her by putting a hose pipe into her mouth from time to time. And make her take it easy with the trunk, as far as you can – hand feed her the fruit and veg. I don't want the stitches breaking out of the skin.'

'Leave it to me, doc,' he replied happily. I knew Ellie was in for a lot of post-operative fussing.

The next day, Sunday, I was sitting at the desk in my office when suddenly the room darkened. I looked up to see the head of an elephant blocking out the sunlight that had been streaming through the window. It was Ellie, of course, but she'd never appeared like that before. I went outside. Ellie turned towards me as I came round the corner of the building and purred. She started to frisk me. Of her keeper there was no sign, but then I heard the sound of footsteps running on the gravel. The keeper, face flushed, came puffing up to us. 'Crikey, doc. She's never done that before – one minute I was cleaning out her straw and the next minute she'd gone, walked out of the door quiet as a church mouse!'

I laughed. 'Perhaps she considers she's an outpatient,' I said. 'Come for a post-op check-up.' I examined the trunk – all was well. The steel sutures were holding.

The keeper led Ellie away by simply holding on gently to the lower edge of an ear between finger and thumb.

On Monday morning she did exactly the same thing and came to see me at the office at about the same time. And again on Tuesday, Wednesday, Thursday and Friday. Simply walked out of the elephant house and plodded the quarter of a mile to where she knew she'd find me. Each day I looked at the trunk, sometimes puffed on more powder, and told her how marvellously well she was doing. The keeper stopped bothering to run after her as soon as she set off, but finished his cleaning before coming to collect her. On the morning of her tenth visit to my office I snipped out the steel sutures. The wound had healed fast and would leave hardly any scar. She could use the trunk as adroitly as ever. Ellie must have rightly considered that the removal of the stitches indicated that I was 'signing her off', for she didn't come to the office the next day, nor ever again.

I remembered what one of my partners in general practice, Trevor Chesworth, had once told me about his father having been prescribed half a bottle of champagne during his convalescence from an operation for nasal polyps. 'It sounds like very sensible medicine,' Trevor had remarked. I agreed. So a few days later I bought a bottle of Mumm, not in this case for the patient, but to split in celebration between the elephant keeper and myself. The patient got a large iced currant bun from Betty's cake shop in Harrogate.

2
The Colonel's Tigers

Or if some time when roaming round,
A noble wild beast greets you,
With black stripes on a yellow ground,
Just notice if he eats you.
This simple rule may help you learn
The Bengal Tiger to discern!

Carolyn Wells, *How to Tell Wild Animals*

What brought matters to a head as far as the parish council was concerned, was young Miss Evans breaking her leg. It was a perfect autumn morning with a sky of duck-egg blue and a low sun whose white blaze could only blunt the sharpness of the clear air with its faint odours of wet leaves and wood smoke. In the far distance beyond Point of Ayr, flocks of waders swirled like clouds of that very smoke above the tide-line as they came in to land on the silt and sand of the Dee estuary.

Miss Evans was, as usual at this time of day, riding her pony along one of the quiet, hedged lanes outside a village of a dozen houses, a pub, a chapel and a shop, some four miles from Prestatyn, the North Wales seaside resort. The pony was of solid build and solid character, inured to the sweeping rains, the winds off the sea and the cold winters that afflict this part of Clwyd, traffic-proof to a fault and, being long in the tooth, wise in the ways of horsy folk and other humans. He knew all the lanes, the fields, the dogs that barked in this cottage, the cat that was ever curled up in the window of that, the sound of Dylan the postie's van, the squawky voice of the farmer who always called a 'mornin' luv' from inside the cowshed when they walked by. In short, he knew the flat countryside between Trelawnyd and the sea, and its inhabitants, like the back of his hoof.

So when, on this particular morning, he first sniffed something new, something very odd, on the damp air and then, almost immediately turned a bend in the lane and came face to face with a tiger, a fully grown tiger of a rich reddy-orange with coal-black stripes and a handsome face with eyes that were truly 'burning bright', he, to put it bluntly, 'freaked out'. Ignoring the fact that the tiger was walking peacefully towards him, innocent of all ill intent, and wearing a collar to which was clipped a strong lead held by a tall silver-haired and moustached man of military bearing, the pony turned, as if it were on a sixpence, and dived through the nearest hedge of brambles. Miss Evans was swept from the saddle and fell hard, breaking a tibia. The pony, uninjured but thunderstruck, galloped straight as a die towards the distant shore, where he was found later in the morning standing exhausted at the water's edge.

Tigers, of course, are not native to Wales, and although there are reports in the press, particularly during the 'silly season' in summer of Surrey pumas, assorted Exmoor beasts and Kellas cats in Scotland, and I've been fruitlessly a-hunting with my dart gun for some of these elusive predators on occasion in the past, there are so far no rumours of tigers on the loose in Great Britain – not even in Clwyd. The tiger in question was not from a zoo, safari park or circus but a pet, one of a pair of pure Bengal tiger pets, each about nine feet long from nose to tail tip and weighing five hundred pounds or so. They belonged to Colonel Mather, and Colonel Mather was stretching the patience of the parish council to the limit. The bolting pony broke that patience, along with Miss Evans's tibia.

The colonel, so I was to learn later when I became involved in the affair, was in his seventies, ex-Indian army and a widower, who had come to live in Britain for the first time in his life only six years earlier. He had bought an isolated Victorian house surrounded by dense clumps of fir trees and was regarded with a mixture of curiosity and awe by the local folk. A gent of the old school, a loner, but meticulously well mannered on the rare occasions that he called in at the pub for a gin and soda, always neatly groomed, obviously military to the bone. Didn't seem to be without a bob or two, but considered to be rather careful with his money according to tradesmen who had occasionally done business with him. An eccentric. Such were the impressions he had created in the little community. Especially *eccentric* – because, you see, he kept *tigers* in the house.

Dylan, the postie, had been the first to see them. 'Sittin' in the bay window – lookin' out if you please. Like they were Siamese or some such!' His account, delivered in the tap room of the Red Dragon, had been received by the assembled company with rapt and silent attention, and had later gained him several pints of John Smith's.

The tigers had been but cubs then, brought over from India by the colonel and quarantined in Southampton, before coming up to North Wales. It was as they grew to maturity that the problems had started for the locals. A man painting window frames on the outside of the colonel's house one summer's day looked down to see two tigers sunning themselves in the grass at the foot of his ladder and stayed up aloft for two hours before he could attract their owner's attention. The colonel had been asleep in a lounge at the back of the house. When he at last heard the man's cries and came to see what all the fuss was, he laughed heartily, patted Rajah and Ranee (they were male and female) on their fine heads, and scolded the poor fellow 'for being so yellow. My babies wouldn't hurt a fly, dammit!' The painter had descended the ladder while the colonel fussed over his purring tigers, and then had run to his van, never to return to finish the job.

A farmer whose land abutted the colonel's swore blind he had sheep mauled to death, throats torn out by something more powerful than a fox or a big dog. But he'd talked of losing sheep like that, folks said, *before* the colonel came to live in the gloomy house among the fir trees. The farmer said he *knew* it was the tigers, but the police never found any proof.

The colonel began to take his big cats for walks on collars and leads at all hours of the day and night across the fields and along the maze of lanes and bridle ways. Their nocturnal strolls soon had an impact on the amatory activities of the local inhabitants, and provided abundant grist for the gossip-mill of the Red Dragon. It did no good at all to a young farmer and his girlfriend, parked in a popular 'lovers' lane', to have their foreplay interrupted by one tiger actually springing on to the warm bonnet of their vehicle and peering in through the windscreen while the other pawed in friendly fashion at the offside window. A certain parish dignitary who suddenly had his bare buttocks licked by the rough file that is the surface of a tiger's tongue, instantly lost all interest in the lady who was not his wife when the tigers came upon them *in flagrante delicto* behind an oak tree. The lady had needed tranquillizing injections from the local GP and had been off work with 'nerves' for a week after the encounter.

Representations were made to the colonel by a trio of villagers comprising the constable, the chapel minister and a councillor. It would be much appreciated if he confined the walking of his tigers to the daytime. Meeting a tiger or two in the darkness could conceivably induce heart attacks in some of the senior citizens. What then?

The colonel, who had received the delegation in a dusty room with walls heavily laden with trophies and weaponry, promised nothing and said little other than that he believed 'Britain was a free country, he was a free man and one, moreover, who had fought for Freedom, King, Country and Empire'.

Next morning the colonel walked into the village shop with

one of the tigers on a lead and at his heel. A man, on the point of leaving with the newspaper and bottle of milk he had purchased, dropped the bottle as the tiger sniffed his trouser leg and, as milk spread over the floor, leaped over the counter almost into the arms of Mrs Cadwallader, the shopkeeper. Made of sterner stuff, Mrs Cadwallader, who was also a fervent lover of cats, watched as the tiger lapped tentatively at the spilt milk. 'You shouldn't bring your tiger in here, colonel,' she said evenly. 'Might scare away custom, I dare say.'

The colonel gave a little bow of his handsome silver-haired head with its aquiline nose and short, waxed moustache, and asked for his monthly supply of Darjeeling tea which Mrs Cadwallader ordered specially from London. 'Rajah here is no alley cat, but a prince of pets. *Noblesse oblige*,' he muttered somewhat cryptically. 'Trouble with this country nowadays, people losing their fibre. Need more of the old English spirit. Henry the Fifth was on target – "We few, we happy few, we band of brothers".'

'I'm sure you're right, colonel,' Mrs Cadwallader handed him his change. 'But, please, don't bring your lovely tigers in the shop again. Upset folk, it can.'

The man sheltering behind her said, rather courageously, 'We're Welsh here, colonel, not English.'

'Henry the Fifth was born in Monmouth, my good man,' snapped the colonel, as he led his pet out of the shop. There was a considerable amount of scuttling indoors and moving of curtains as man and tiger walked away at a brisk pace.

The colonel didn't take his tiger shopping in the village in the days that followed, but matters didn't improve. He still went walking in the neighbourhood with one or both of the tigers, and the number of people who were at least surprised, if not scared out of their wits, by coming across the animals out of the blue, steadily climbed. There was a furore at the golf club when he actually walked the pair across the eighteenth fairway when the captain was on the point of teeing off. Then Rajah, the male, peed backwards as is the way with tigers and domestic toms, soaking the bench in the village bus shelter and impregnating it with the pungent, rank smell of tiger to such a degree that for several days passengers preferred to stand in the pouring rain to await the Prestatyn bus.

A more serious accident was the killing of a whippet belonging to one of the local poachers. The dog had pursued a rabbit into the colonel's garden where Rajah and Ranee were roaming free while the colonel watched, gin and soda in hand, from a deckchair at tiffin time. Nimble as both rabbit and whippet were, the tigers were nimbler. Ranee got one with a bound and a cuff of a heavy paw. Rajah got the other. The colonel was very tetchy about the affair when the poacher called at the house after making sure that the tigers were safely indoors. He rambled on about how the ending of National Service was to blame for producing the poacher and other good-for-nothings, but he stumped up thirty pounds to pay for a new dog.

Then Miss Evans broke her leg, and at the next meeting of the parish council the colonel's tigers were at the top of the agenda. It was unanimously agreed that any tiger was *persona non grata* in peaceful Clwyd. Something had to be done about it. The chairman had a bright idea – get the RSPCA to sort it out. 'After all,' he said, silently recalling the tiger licking his bottom, 'perhaps cruelty is involved.' How was the colonel keeping the beasts *inside* the house? And the death of the poacher's dog was surely a cruel one. 'And,' he lowered his voice to a chilling whisper, 'might they not turn into man-eaters?' The chapel minister supported the chairman's dire warning. He had found a book in the travelling library written by the famous big-game hunter Jim Corbett. He read out to the enthralled meeting selected passages on Corbett's adventures with man-eating tigers. There was no need for further discussion after that. The RSPCA would be contacted without delay.

Once upon a time, until the Dangerous Wild Animals Act

came into force in Britain in 1976, anyone could keep a
tiger – or a Tasmanian devil, or a gorilla – in the spare
bedroom or garden shed. Provided they weren't actually
cruel to the beast, which could be dealt with though often
with difficulty, under the Cruelty to Animals Act, and it
didn't rampage around the land causing mayhem, nothing
much could be done about it. Since 1976, however, it has
been illegal to keep certain species on private property
without a licence from the local authority, a licence which is
only granted after inspections carried out by a veterinary
surgeon and, usually, an environmental health officer. The
list of species covered by the Act is very broad, and besides
such obvious animals as tigers, elephants and crocodiles,
also includes kangaroos, camels, emus and sealions. Yes, I
know a man who has a licence to keep a pet sealion in the
backyard of his pub in Yorkshire.

A few years ago Dumbarton Council in Scotland asked
me to inspect the facilities of a showbiz personality, a
hypnotist, who wanted a licence for the two tigers and one
emu that he lived with in a bungalow not far from Loch
Lomond. It turned out that the 'facilities' were nothing
more than a small bedroom allotted to each. No barred
windows, no other modifications whatever to the property.
I strongly advised the council to reject the licence
application.

Colonel Mather and his pair of tigers were disturbing the
rustic harmony of the North Wales village some years
before the Act came into force.

In due course an RSPCA inspector from Chester arrived in
the village and together with the constable paid a call on the
colonel. It was a very brief visit. The colonel stood in the
doorway while the constable politely tucked his helmet
under one arm and outlined the council's concerns. Might
the RSPCA inspector be permitted to cast an eye over the
tigers and their quarters? The latter was secretly very very
relieved (he'd only ever seen tigers in a zoo) when the

colonel responded by shouting, 'Stuff and nonsense! Be off!' and banged the door shut. As the two men turned to trudge away, they caught sight of a tiger looking through a bay window. The room behind it was littered with broken furniture, upholstery shredded. The curtains beside the tiger's noble head hung in tattered streamers.

Later that day telephone discussions went on between the constable's superior officer and RSPCA headquarters. As a matter of human, as well as animal, welfare it was decided that Colonel Mather should receive a second visit, this time with a warrant to enter the premises and a vet with a dart gun standing by. So it was that I came to drive over from Rochdale through a chill early morning fog with my tranquillizing equipment in the boot of the car and the intention of having a few oysters at Bolland's in Chester on the way back.

There were two RSPCA men, a police inspector and the village constable gathered outside the Red Dragon when I arrived late because of the fog. The police inspector introduced everyone and then described his strategy. 'I'll go in alone,' he said sounding like a tough cop about to burst in on Al Capone. 'Humour the old chap. Get him to see sense. You lot will wait at the bottom of the drive. When I call you, come up to the house. Shouldn't be a problem. And if there's the slightest excuse for seizing the tigers, you, doc, will dart 'em and the RSPCA will take 'em away in their van.'

'Hold on a moment,' I said. '*If* it comes to that, what are the RSPCA going to do with them? Stick them in their kennels? The animals will sleep long enough under the Sernylan I will use. But when they wake up, what then? Tigers aren't stray poodles or homeless cats.'

'We thought of taking them to Chester Zoo,' said one of the RSPCA men.

'Have you contacted them?'

'Well, no, not yet. Not till we see what the situation is.'

'I suggest we get on the phone now before we go

anywhere.' Old Mr Mottershead, Chester Zoo's then
director, was not one to take lightly the arrival of a pair of
adult tigers at his back gate without warning. 'Tiger
accommodation, secure and spacious enough, is not as
easily found as a disused parrot cage or a fish tank,' I said
and went to the telephone box. As I expected, Chester Zoo
had no vacant accommodation for tigers, but the director at
Belle Vue in Manchester agreed to take the animals
temporarily, should it be necessary, until a permanent home
could be found.

'Smashing!' said the police inspector, becoming flushed
with excitement, I thought. 'Wagons roll!'

I drove along behind the RSPCA van and police car. It
took us some ten minutes to reach the colonel's house
hidden within its dark green mantle of firs and approached
by a dirt track that led off a narrow no-through road. A
sign at the gateway to the drive bore the words NO
HAWKERS, TRESPASSERS, GYPSIES OR JEHOVAH'S WITNESSES.

We waited while the police inspector walked up the drive
towards the house that lay out of view round a sharp bend.
It was twenty minutes before we saw him again, hurriedly
walking back, his face pale and stern. 'Bloody old fool's got
a gun!' he blurted out when he reached us. 'Constable, get
the station on the radio. We need reinforcements.'

It appeared that after a lengthy and increasingly heated
exchange, conducted as before on the doorstep, with the
colonel ranting on about how the nation was going to the
dogs and giving a lurid description of the way he once
horse-whipped an insolent Hindu policeman, he had
grabbed a shotgun that was lying on a table in the hall and
stuck the barrels almost up the inspector's right nostril. 'I'm
a free man,' he had shouted, the gun barrels not wavering in
the slightest. 'Get off back to your damned socialist village
council and tell 'em that!' He had kept the shotgun trained
on the police inspector's back until he turned the bend in
the drive.

Within half an hour we were joined by what seemed to be

most of the North Wales police force including the chief constable and a squad of marksmen in dark blue flak jackets. The track to the drive gates was cluttered with cars, blue lights flashing prettily in the rising mist.

After being briefed on the earlier events the chief constable leaned back against the bonnet of a police Land-Rover and conducted a council of war.

'Seems to me we've got a loony old chappie here,' he said. 'He's got access to a gun or guns. Don't know if he'd use 'em, but can't take the chance. Tigers in the house – we've got the vet and the RSPCA to take care of them. So it should be a matter of jaw-jaw. Talking the old bird into seeing sense. We'll have our men all round the house in the trees, with the marksmen evenly spread among them, just in case. I'll go up to the front door when everyone is in place. I'll be very surprised if he doesn't come quietly. I was in India myself during the war. Those regular officers who'd been there since the year dot could be a funny lot, but I think I understand how they tick. Empire and pig-sticking and durbars and all that.'

'What happens if he lets the tigers loose on us, sir?' asked a constable when he stopped speaking.

There was a brief period of complete silence. Then the chief constable said, 'The vet here will use his dart gun and sedate them.'

'Unlike what you see on well-edited Tarzan films,' I cautioned, 'tranquillizing darts don't work instantly. The drug has to travel from the injection point to the brain before it can work. That takes at least two or three minutes.'

'Time enough to be eaten!' murmured someone behind me.

The chief constable frowned, lit a Camel and thought for a few moments. 'OK,' he said. 'I'll go up to the front door with the vet, his dart gun loaded. From what I hear the tigers are in a room to the left of the door. If there's any trouble with the beasts the vet can dart 'em by breaking the window, or outside if they leave the house. I'll have a marksman covering the vet. If the knock-out darts don't do the trick or aren't quick enough, we'll kill the bastards.'

A few minutes later, the police having dispersed at the double to their positions surrounding the house, the chief constable, a marksman and I began slowly walking up the drive. I felt a bit like Wyatt Earp at the OK Corral (I assume Wyatt Earp was nervous!). My dart rifle had a loaded syringe of Sernylan in the barrel and there were three spare loaded syringes in my pocket.

'If it comes for us, a tiger I mean,' whispered the marksman as the house of dark stone came into sight, 'what's best to aim for, head or heart?'

'Whatever's available,' I replied. 'They move so fast when they attack, you won't have time to choose.'

'STOP WHERE YOU ARE!' The voice came from an upstairs window. It was the voice of a man accustomed to giving orders. The three of us halted immediately in our tracks. I could see a silver-haired man standing at the open window pointing a shotgun towards us. Clearly visible, ranged along the window sill, were the upright barrels of a pair of .308s. 'I know what you're here for!' the colonel continued as we looked up at him. 'You want to kill my babies, my fine tigers.'

'Not at all, sir,' the chief constable adopted a soothing, conciliatory tone of voice. 'Goodness me no, sir.'

'If that's the case, what are you here for?'

'Sir, it's your tigers – wonderful animals, seen 'em myself many times in India – your tigers, sir, are causing difficulties for the local community.'

'What difficulties?'

'Well, sir, if you'd put that gun down and let me in, we could discuss . . .'

'Balderdash! You're out to kill my babies.'

'No sir, believe me.'

The colonel turned his head slightly and fixed his gaze first upon me and then on the marksman. 'If you aren't out to kill my tigers,' the old soldier sounded colder, slyer, 'why are those minions of yours carrying firearms?'

'This gentleman, sir, is a vet. His gun is a dart gun, not for killing.'

'A horse-doctor, dammit?' He addressed me. I could see his eyes. Blue as cornflowers, unblinking. 'Only horse-doctors I'd trust were in the Veterinary Corps. Are you a riding man, eh?'

'I can ride,' I said. 'But not well.'

'Ever been up the Hindu Kush?'

'Never, sir.'

'Well, you're not going to kill my tigers. Seen horse-doctors kill too many good horses in Baluchistan.'

'Sir,' said the chief constable. 'Can't we talk about all this without any guns being involved?'

'Nothing to talk about. Get off my property!'

I glanced to my left. Two Bengal tigers had their nose pads pressed to the window pane of a shadow-filled room. Typical cats.

'May I look at your tigers here, sir?' I called. 'They seem fine specimens.' Before he could answer I moved slowly over to the long-uncleaned window.

'BOOM!' There was the loud report of a shotgun. I ducked involuntarily and looked around to see the chief constable and the marksman crouching on the ground. The colonel's smoking gun was pointing towards the sky. 'You're not going to kill my tigers,' he shouted. 'Next time it won't be a warning shot!'

The chief constable stood up, his voice no longer conciliatory. 'Colonel Mather. My marksman here, and there are others in the trees, will shoot you the moment you point your weapon at any one of us. Listen carefully. No one will kill your tigers, I promise you. The vet is going to tranquillize them with his dart gun – when I tell him to. Remember, if you do no more than point the gun at him, the police marksmen here will shoot you without further warning.'

It was as if the colonel had suddenly been sucked dry of all energy. His shoulders slumped as he let his arms drop and the shotgun disappeared from view.

'Do it, doc!' said the chief constable *sotto voce* and I broke the window pane with a short jab of the Cap-Chur rifle barrel and fired a dart point-blank into one of the tigers. It gave a roar like a beat of a bass drum and bounded to the far side of the room. Opening the clumsy breech of the rifle with trembling fingers, I somehow managed to insert another dart into the barrel, closed it and aimed at the other tiger which had run to the side of its mate. The dart hit it square on the side of the neck. There had been no further sound from the colonel or his gun, I suddenly realized, when at last after about four minutes both tigers lay unconscious.

It all ended with a hurly-burly of people bustling into the house. The RSPCA men and I carried the tigers out to their van. I injected a top-up dose of Sernylan for the one-and-a-half-hour journey to Manchester. Policemen swirled through every room, looking for goodness knows what, the odd vampire bat or mammoth perhaps. The colonel, looking so very old and sad, but every inch an upright English gent, was taken un-handcuffed to a car that had raced up to the front door.

When it was all over I felt exhausted and drove straight back home to Rochdale, forgoing the oysters.

Colonel Mather appeared in court some weeks later and was conditionally discharged on all charges. There was no question of there having been any cruelty. The tigers were in excellent condition, though their living quarters, the front room with its unbarred windows and rickety wooden door, were frighteningly insecure. The court ruled that they constituted a threat to public order and should not return to the house among the fir trees. They lived out the rest of their lives, and bred, at a safari park in the south of England. The colonel died within the year – from a broken heart at the loss of his 'babies' – or so the tap room at the Red Dragon had it.

The incident of Colonel Mather and his tigers was later to form the main thread of one episode of BBC Television's drama series 'One by One', which was based on my work with wild animals. Nowadays, there is not a single tiger in private hands in this country which, I guess, is just as well for all concerned.

Tigers and other big cats, with the exception of cheetahs, do not present special problems for their doctors now that chemical control of them is safe, precise and flexible since the introduction of reversible anaesthetics. When I was a student things were very different; no flying syringes, no injectable anaesthetics except barbiturates which were dangerous, not least because they were irreversible and could only be injected when the animal was approachable, to wit too seriously ill to cause a fuss, or if a special 'crush' cage was *in situ*. Many zoos and other big cat owners didn't have one of the latter in the fifties and early sixties.

At one time nutritional disease was common in these creatures. Fed mainly on raw meat which is rich in phosphorus but low in calcium, other minerals, vitamins and some important trace elements, exotic felines suffered all manner of disease syndromes including rickets and various forms of blindness. Now, with mineral and vitamin supplements added regularly to their diet and quantities of bone, whole chicken and oily fish like herring provided from time to time, I rarely see dietary ailments.

The infectious diseases of exotic cats are in general similar to those of your fireside familiar, though there is more risk of salmonellosis where knacker meat is fed, or there is contact with water or grassland contaminated by rodents.

Such cats are, therefore, the easiest species for the budding zoo vet to begin with. Except, as I say, for the cheetah. These most elegant and speedy of cats that were once tamed as 'hunting leopards' – no Italian renaissance court was without them – are different from their feline relatives in many ways. The pupils of their eyes are round and their claws, unlike those of other cats, including domestic ones, cannot be retracted. I have also found the streamlined, leggy hunters to be rather delicate – quick to fall ill, slow to recover and heir to diseases 'of their own'. The commonest and most dangerous of these is a form of liver disease whose cause, possibly a virus or toxic agent, has yet to be identified.

Much as I love all the representatives of the dog family with which I come in contact – the wolves, jackals and foxes – I love the cat family more, and my greatest pleasure is being able actually to touch a cheetah, a tiger or a clouded leopard. But then, like half the British population, I'm a cat person through and through.

3

In the Shadow of the Circus

The behaviour of men to the lower animals, and their
behaviour to each other, bear a constant relationship.

Herbert Spencer, nineteenth-century English philosopher,
in *Social Statics*

There are some species of animal which, whatever one's
opinion of circuses, should not be part of 'The Greatest
Show on Earth'. Bears, hippos, rhinos and giraffes are
among them. From the very beginning of my work with
exotic animals I have regularly come across touring circuses
that carried with them, often as part of the 'menagerie',
wagons full of non-performing animals, an amazing
assortment of creatures, some rare and endangered, all kept
in conditions far worse than those of even the shabbiest
zoo.

Such animals lived all their lives in cramped cages,
occasionally literally boxes, that were trundled from town
to town and country to country, seemingly unprotected by
the rules and regulations that increasingly, but still not
sufficiently, govern the keeping of animals in zoos, farms,
riding stables, pet shops and the like. Britain has its Zoo
Act and Dangerous Wild Animal Act. The former, with its
system of official inspections, has led to the closure of zoos
that did not come up to the government's standards, the
latter has put paid to folk who fancied keeping tiger cubs in
their bedrooms or raising a baby chimp along with their
own offspring. Celebrities, such as the famous showjumper
who kept young lions, their claws removed, badly, in a
horse-box, or the disc jockey with the monkey that was

perpetually stoned on dope, must now quench their overweening thirst for self-publicity in other ways.

However, circuses are exempt. A zoo cannot keep a gorilla in a ten foot by ten foot metal cage – a circus can. A private owner cannot walk a tiger on a lead down a street without a licence – a circus can. Only the laws relating to cruelty to animals in general apply to circuses, and bodies such as the RSPCA have for long failed to notch up even one conviction against circuses for cruelty under the Act.

British circuses, although perhaps only Gerry Cottle's and Gandey's are in the same league as the best ones on the continent – Krone Knie, Americano – are far better at caring for their animals than many in Spain, Italy or Greece. One reason for this is the existence of the Association of Circus Proprietors, a body set up by some of the most illustrious names in British circus – Chipperfield, Smart and Mills. For many years Andrew, one of my partners, and I have been veterinary advisers to the Association. 'How can you work with those people?' we have sometimes been asked. 'Animal exploiters at their worst. Lions in beast wagons all their lives. Elephants that never roam free.' Maybe. But the lions and the elephants need medical care. To deny them that would simply worsen their lot. While I would not defend the use of snow leopards, bears, gorillas, rhinos, chimps and many other species in a circus, they deserve expert attention so long as they *are* there, no less than their relatives in Regent's Park or San Diego Zoo. Our relationship with the major British circuses through the Association has meant that at least some standards for animal health and well-being have been introduced. A touring circus with a sick animal once had to call in a different vet, usually one without any exotic animal experience, in every town it visited. Supervision, diagnosis and treatment were, at best, chaotic. Now we can coordinate the handling of medical cases by telephone calls to local vets, or if need be by travelling to wherever the Big Top has been pitched.

Most importantly, we have gradually introduced standards for the housing and management of Association animals, standards which are being increasingly acted upon by the younger members of the circus families as the conservative old guard take a back seat. Each Association circus is inspected at least twice a year by either Andrew or myself, and we can make unannounced spot checks whenever so minded. Driving around the country on other work, particularly during the summer, we often come across a circus encampment, and will go in to have a look at the animals and the conditions. With the Association we set up a list of standards that must be achieved if a circus is to receive our certificate and retain its membership of the organization – and membership is important, for without it some local authorities will not give permission to 'build up' the tent on council land.

Our inspection system for the Association is, of course, a self-policing arrangement at present, but it has definitely resulted in improved conditions for many circus animals. Andrew and I decided to proceed cautiously, recommending minimum dimensions for the wagons that house and transport the big cats, the cessation of menageries displaying non-performing animals, and the provision of exercise paddocks (with electric-wire fencing as used on farms) for elephants, and exercise annexes for lions, tigers and bears. To my delight, and some surprise, the circus owners agreed and, what was more, put our recommendations into practice. At the time of an inspection we will look at such things as the condition of the tenting, over the animal rather than the public areas, the loose boxes and wooden flooring in the horse and elephant lines (any rotting there that might help the onset of foot disease?), lift horse blankets to check for hidden saddle sores, and demand access to transport vehicles (clean and secure?) and food supplies (adequate in quality and quantity?). I had the membership of a famous English circus turned down a few years ago because it was carrying not one bale of hay for feeding in an emergency to its elephants, should anything go wrong with its usual policy of buying provender locally as it toured from town to town. We look over every poodle playing in the team of 'footballing dogs', and keep an eye open for the lesions behind an elephant's ears that would indicate someone is employing a viciously pointed 'elephant hook'.

All animals at the circus during our visit are inspected, except for domestic pets in caravans. Visiting 'guest' acts – a troupe of Liberty horses from Denmark or Mary Chipperfield's white tigers – must also all be up to scratch in condition, housing, feeding and management if the host circus is to get its certificate. As a young vet beginning circus work in the late Fifties I was regularly cursed and threatened by paranoid big cat 'tamers' and treated with unconcealed contempt by secretive elephant men, breeds which thankfully have become almost completely extinct. Nowadays my relationship with the young new generation of circus people is open and constructive, and very similar to that between me and zoo staff.

But I return to the point I made earlier about the difference in the statutory requirements for standards of animal care between circuses and zoos. It isn't merely a question of legislation, or the lack of it, it simply is not physically possible to do *the best* for animals in circuses. Circuses can never truly be mobile zoos possessing all the qualities of good static ones. Knowing what we do now about the basic requirements of wild creatures, it is increasingly difficult to defend animal-using circuses, and I detect the first signs of their slow but steady demise, certainly in Britain. They have had their day. Abroad, however, circuses good and bad still flourish in many countries.

It was another of those surreal days – maybe if I pinched myself even harder I would wake up from one of those dreams which are a composite of individual rational occurrences put together by a madman, a bizarre whole constructed from fragments of normality, as if a chimpanzee had been let loose on a jigsaw puzzle.

'So you must always buy *parmigiano* as a complete round, *dottore*,' the old Italian gentleman was saying, eyes twinkling and moustache twitching appreciatively as he scooped out the last sliver of cheese to leave a bowl formed of the rind alone. 'Then you can put your pasta *inside* the *formaggio*, like this.' He tipped the pan of spaghetti. My knee was aching where the gorilla had whacked it hard. The English girl sat next to me frowning as she fingered an unwelcome ladder in her fishnet tights, and two clowns in full motley and greasepaint squatted on the floor watching 'Dallas' on TV in a language they couldn't understand one word of, and drinking Metaxas straight out of a bottle they passed between them.

Outside the caravan the wind blew in from the iron-grey sea, and stirred up the loose surface of the rubbish tip on which we were camped. Looking out of the window I could see the raw concrete wall of a football stadium and above that a strip of leaden sky. The first raindrops tapped on the roof.

'Never waste the smallest part of *parmigiano* rind, *dottore*,' continued the Italian passing me a plate of *pasta al pesto*. 'Drop it into whatever sauce you are cooking. A glass of Amarone, *dottore*?' He glanced towards the window. 'It doesn't look too good out there, *dottore*.'

It certainly didn't look good out there. And I wasn't thinking of the storm that was gathering in the May sky. Out there in the huddle of painted wagons and the tents of dirty flapping canvas, things were positively bad. The circus, standing for two weeks on the municipal rubbish dump just outside the town of Khalkis on the Greek island of Euboea some fifty miles from Athens, held a dark and dismal secret.

It had all begun some days before. At home in Richmond I had been telephoned by a young woman – the one with the laddered tights. She was, she said, a dancer with the

Circo Coruña. I'd never heard of them. It was apparently an Italian outfit with a Spanish name, but then, circuses are always changing their identities. 'Will you please come to Athens straight away?' the girl had said. 'We've got problems with Luigi, our gorilla.'

A gorilla, one of a species threatened with extinction and heavily protected, theoretically, by the Convention on International Trade in Endangered Species, in a circus! I had seen gorillas before in an Italian circus – a poor couple carted about Europe in the woefully small trailer that was part of the menagerie of Circo Medrano. 'What seems to be the trouble?' I asked.

'On and off he's got diarrhoea. Had it for weeks.'

Calls from circuses and sometimes small zoos that we've never heard of are not uncommon. I suppose I receive two or three a year. Air tickets to destinations such as Athens are anything but cheap, and bitter experience has taught me that circuses and bad debts frequently go together. But we can't refuse a call for help where an animal is ill or in pain. It isn't a matter of Royal College rules, more of a sense of being *responsible* for wild animals in trouble, not in any pious, sanctimonious way but simply because there's no one else to do the job. I began thirty-five years ago to create what was essentially a new profession – that of independent peripatetic wild animal veterinarian. My fascination with untamed beasts and their health problems slowly created a demand for such a specialized service, one that the veterinary general practitioners could not adequately provide. As the number of full-time wild animal vets grew – though even today we number but a few dozen worldwide – so I found myself on duty around the clock every day of the year. If I was right, and I believe I was and still am, in saying that wild animals need specialist care of equal quality to that available for domestic and farm animals, then I could not in all conscience ever turn down a call by referring the case to a local 'dog and cat' or 'farm' vet. And besides, I really could not rest easy in Richmond if I thought that somewhere there was a potbellied pig or a porcupine or a puma in trouble. Or a gorilla in a third-rate little Italian circus on the edge of the Aegean Sea . . .

And so I'd flown to Athens where the circus owner, *Signore* Palmoni, who was now instructing me in the finer points of pasta cookery over a first-class lunch in his caravan, had met me at the airport with a large placard inscribed '*Dott.* Taylor for Gorilla' and driven me to Khalkis in a battered pick-up truck. Khalkis, the main town of the largest of the Aegean islands, is a down-at-heel, grey and gloomy place, and the lowering clouds and brisk chilly wind emphasized the gloom as we arrived at the circus squatting in the centre of the municipal rubbish heap. I had never before met the Italians who ran the circus, but they turned out a kindly, cheerful family who insisted that I must take coffee and *amarettini* with them before getting down to business. Although hospitable to a fault and effusive in their gratitude for my visit even before I'd clapped eyes on the patient, the warm twinkles in their eyes became wary glints when I posed a question. 'Where did you obtain your gorilla, *signore*?'

The Italian gentleman seemed abruptly to lose his more than adequate command of English. He turned to his son and fired off a short brisk sentence in Italian. '*Dottore*,' said the young man, 'what you mean obtain?'

'Get – where did the gorilla come from?'

Father and son, faces solemn now, conversed again in rapid unintelligible Italian. Eventually, with the father having apparently seriously mislaid his English and no mistake, the son curled his mouth into a wondrous crescent moon of a smile and turned to me. 'Papa says Luigi came from the zoo.'

'Oh really? Which zoo? Was he born there?'

'Yes, he came from the zoo.'

'A zoo in Italy?'

'Errr . . . the zoo director knows how good we look after

our animals. Five, how you say er, generations, of our family in circus business. Everyone knows how good we look after all our animals. Like you can say animals is our blood. You understand. *Capisce?*'

The father nodded vigorously and muttered something with his clenched hand held to his heart like an American president at the raising of the Stars and Stripes. They weren't about to give me the name of the 'zoo', I realized. But then, sure as eggs is eggs the 'zoo' didn't exist. Nevertheless, let's get on with the little game, I thought. Let's pretend the gorilla hadn't been smuggled in as a baby after its parents had been killed by poachers. 'How old is Luigi now?'

'Six years, *dottore*,' replied the old man, suddenly coming upon his English once more. 'No happier healthier gorilla on the world. One of the family, one of the Palmones.' Both men now wore those lunar smiles.

'And how old was he when you first got him?'

'Six months,' said the father. 'Two years,' said the son, simultaneously. Confusion as the smiles vanished and they bickered tetchily together in Italian.

'Why did the zoo not want to keep him?' I continued.

That was it – the father's English really did a runner this time. '*No capisco, dottore*,' he said shaking his head.

'My father says it's a pity you don't speak Italian, *dottore* – he would like to tell you how good he looks after all his animals, like his father, his grandfather, his great-grandfather before him.'

The old man stood up. '*Andiamo*,' he said, taking my half-empty cup of coffee.

'Let us go look at Luigi,' said his son. 'We are so glad you have come to see him, *dottore*.'

We walked across to a grey-painted circus wagon. Ascending a short flight of wooden steps, the younger Palmone inserted a key into the steel door of the wagon and immediately pandemonium erupted from within. My ears were deafened by the crashing of metal, a series of explosive thuds that shook the wagon's frame and a chorus of piercing shrieks. It was as if behind the door a host of banshees were clustered around Vulcan at his forge. The young Palmone hesitated before opening the door and screwed his face into a grimace. 'When we go in, *dottore*,' he shouted against the din, 'press yourself against the wall of the wagon to keep out of reach of them. They have long arms.'

The door swung open and he entered, followed closely by me and then his father. The noise was unimaginable. Ears protesting in pain, I flattened myself at once against the door as it closed behind us and sucked in my stomach when horny black fingers snatched at my navel with millimetres to spare. We were in a narrow corridor. Facing us were two rows of small iron cages, one on top of the other. The bars of the cages were thicker and broader than the spaces between them, spaces through which sprouted a small thicket of black and hairy arms, hands clawing at the air. Each cage contained a chimpanzee. At one end of the corridor behind a door of stout bars was a small room, perhaps six feet square, and in it, thumping the floor with clenched fists, was a gorilla – a male of about six or seven years of age. He looked at me with dark and glistening eyes while he thumped out his powerful regular beat. His expression was utterly impassive. Unlike the chimpanzees he uttered no vocal sound.

'Slide along the wall, *dottore*,' shouted Palmone junior as his father, who had acquired an iron tent peg from somewhere, added to the din by beating it against the chimp cage bars. 'Slide along and keep your belly in.'

I slid sideways towards the gorilla and when the lock of his door was opened kept sliding right into his tiny room.

Luigi was a powerfully built young gorilla with a mouthful of strong yellow teeth. There wasn't much room inside his quarters for two adult humans as well as him – old Palmone had stayed in the corridor. His tent peg had eventually silenced the chimpanzees and now he stood in front of the bank of cages brandishing the thing menacingly. Luigi sniffed my trousers and prodded my groin with a hard index finger. I saw that the floor was heavily smeared with yellow diarrhoea and there was the typical sour and pungent smell of a gorilla with upset bowels.

'He's had every medicine we could think of, *dottore*,' said my companion as I looked down at the gorilla who was crouched looking up at me. 'But Greek vets know nothing about monkeys like Luigi. He's had penicillin and streptomycin and chloramphenicol and . . .' he reeled off a list of ten or a dozen more antibiotics. '. . . and a pharmacist in Crete said that an extract of herbs was certain to work and my wife's mother in Southend in England posted some powder that her doctor said was good for enteritis, a vet in Athens said it was salmonella for sure, but didn't want to examine Luigi. He charged two hundred dollars for some pink medicine. That didn't help. Then another vet – he also said he didn't want to look at Luigi – said for sure it was worms and told me to give him nothing to drink for five days and then a yellow capsule, big as a hen's egg – Luigi wouldn't take it – nor the meat tea that a hospital doctor here in Khalkis advised. So, *dottore*, what is wrong with poor Luigi?'

'Does he live all the time in here?' I asked.

'Except when he is working in the show, yes.'

'What does he do in the show?'

The young Italian laughed. 'Luigi? He is a star. He is the special, the best. All the people love him. You will see when you come to the next performance.'

Luigi was now holding my right ankle in a vice-like grip and still looking up at me. What was going on behind the mask-like face with those limpid knowing eyes? 'So he's worked all the time during his illness?'

'Yes. He would be sad if he didn't go into the ring, *dottore*. And the people *expect* him, they come to see *him*.'

I remembered the circus posters I'd seen pasted up on walls as we drove through the town. The illustration was dominated by a King Kong type of creature towering above a tent half its size and snarling ferociously. The gorilla holding my ankle was the King Kong lookalike – and about the size of an adult male chimpanzee. 'I'd like to examine him more closely,' I said.

The Italian pursed his lips and shrugged his shoulders. 'We can try,' he said. 'But he can be, how you say, awkward.'

At that point Luigi released my ankle and with the thereby unencumbered hand punched me soundly in the solar plexus. Winded, I doubled over and the gorilla, timing precisely the effect of his blow, grabbed a bunch of my none-too-plentiful hair as my head descended, and yanked it out. Regaining my breath at last, I straightened up. Luigi still crouched at my feet. His expression had not changed – or had it? Was it my imagination or were his eyes really sparkling? He certainly didn't look at all cross or upset.

'Naughty Luigi,' said Palmone. He gave the gorilla a soft smack on the back of his shoulders. Luigi thereupon reached up and delivered a sweet short jab to *his* solar plexus and it was the Italian's turn to buckle at the midriff.

Luigi glanced at me – the eyes *were* sparkling, I was sure of it. Behind me old Palmone began to bang his tent peg against the door in an attempt to induce a more respectful attitude on the part of Luigi. The gorilla shuffled slowly on feet and knuckles towards the door and then, quick as a flash, shot an arm out between the bars and withdrew it – holding the tent peg like a field marshal's baton. '*Porca Madonna!*' yelled the old man.

'Luigi – give me that,' said his son in Italian. Luigi did – he cracked him smartly with the tent peg, first on one foot and then the other. Then he swiftly hid the metal stake under a pile of his straw bedding and returned to sit at my feet, quiet and composed, as if butter wouldn't melt in his mouth. The younger Palmone hopped painfully from foot to foot. '*Maledetto sia!*' he hissed. 'Do you think it is possible to examine him, *dottore?*'

I had come a long way to see Luigi; to return without laying hands on him was unthinkable. Employing a tranquillizing drug might well mask important symptoms, such as inhibiting Luigi from revealing a painful spot when I prodded it – probably by knocking my front teeth out, I reflected ruefully. Time for the secret weapon. I put my hand in my pocket and pulled out a packet that I had purchased at Heathrow airport. Breaking it open I extracted and unwrapped one of the cunning devices which would have been invaluable to Sigourney Weaver in *Gorillas in the Mist*. I held it out for Luigi's inspection. He eyed it beadily, sniffed it, and presently took it gently between finger and thumb and popped it into his mouth. The big gorilla began to suck and then crunch appreciatively on the Fox's Glacier Mint. I slowly bent down and first stroked the gorilla's head before pulling down one of his lower eyelids to inspect the conjunctiva – paler than normal. I put a finger between his lips and exposed an area of his gums – also pale. Luigi shot out a hand, palm up. He wanted another mint. I gave him the sweet and then continued my examination. Crunch, crunch went Luigi, content and relaxed as I took his pulse and cautiously pressed a finger into his stomach, probing for lumps or an enlarged liver. Nothing. The gorilla finished his fifth mint and then, considering me too slow in delivering the goodies, hooked a finger over the edge of my jacket pocket, neatly ripped it off and caught the bag of mints as it fell out. He was the model patient. '*Incredibile!*' murmured young Palmone. 'What you give, *dottore*? A sedative?'

I explained to him that the only bit of information on exotic animals I'd been given at university nearly forty years before had been from the late Professor Sir William Weipers, one of my heroes in the veterinary world and the man who had made the Glasgow Veterinary School the finest in the land. He had described how he had found that Fox's Glacier Mints (the brand was important it seemed) would charm almost any creature. He'd just been treating wallabies in a Scottish park for frostbite of their tails and, typically, his handling of these timid creatures had been greatly facilitated by a constant supply of the transparent ice-cube-like sweets.

The physical examination over, I took a sample bottle from my other intact pocket and scooped in some of Luigi's freshly passed diarrhoea. 'OK, done for now,' I said and gently patted Luigi, who had just finished the last of the mints, on his crewcut pate. He looked up at me once more – and swung a left hook that connected with my kneecap and might have knocked it flying across the tiny room – or so it felt. Hobbling in agony, I opened the door and limped out.

Back in the circus bosses' caravan over a restorative *grappa* and tablet of Ponstan, I rubbed my throbbing kneecap and told the Palmones that I needed to find a laboratory, or at least a microscope, while the stool sample was still fresh.

It wasn't easy. The young Palmone drove me into the town. It was lunchtime and the hospital's laboratory was locked up for the day. The first two vets we found didn't possess microscopes and the third had one whose objective lenses were lost and was thus useless. By three o'clock, however, we had tracked down a medical practitioner who had a fine nineteenth-century brass microscope sitting on a shelf in his consulting room as a decorative antique rather than a scientific instrument. The microscope worked, and in a drawer the doctor found me the broken half of a glass microscope slide. I put a little blob of Luigi's diarrhoeic stool on the slide and after adding a couple of drops of saline solution, teased the mixture with a needle before putting the preparation under the microscope's low-power lens. I peered down through the eyepiece and twiddled the big brass wheel. The disc of light from the mirror angled towards the consulting-room window brightened and a collection of magnified objects jumped into focus looking like flotsam on a shallow tide. I could see lengths of rope-like undigested plant fibre and one or two seemingly deflating rugby footballs – the eggs of pin worms and not likely to be causing trouble. There were some pretty pollen grains and a single cell resembling a fried egg. This latter was an amoeba, but after scrutinizing it for a few minutes I found that it moved too slowly to be the disease-producing *Entamoeba histolytica* and contained within it, unlike the latter, a prominent nucleus and no gobbled-up red blood cell. I concluded that it was a harmless *Entamoeba coli*, a common denizen of gorilla – and human – bowels. I moved the slide to examine another field. A small flotilla of round vessels – Welsh coracles without crew on board – travelled on a zigzag course across the disc of light and vanished. I moved the slide again and caught up with them. Oval in shape and with shimmering hulls they sailed erratically onwards. More of them, dozens, came into view. They bumped and bounced into one another like rubber dinghies on a pond. That was what I was looking for. The moving oval 'boats' were protozoan parasites, microscopical one-celled creatures that propel themselves by means of rows of 'oars', fine hairlike structures called cilia, that give their 'hulls' the appearance of shimmering as they scull along. *Balantidium*, the name of the old foe that I'd encountered several times before, in chimps, gibbons and monkeys as well as gorillas, was the cause of Luigi's illness.

I told Palmone to look down the microscope and explained the significance of the minute moving organisms. 'Luigi will be cured within three days,' I said. 'All we need is a drug we are sure to find at any pharmacy in Khalkis.'

Back at the circus I warned the Palmones that *Balantidium* was a highly infectious little beast that might easily spread to humans as well as to other primates.

'Please come then and look over all our other animals, *dottore*,' said the old man, his English rediscovered yet again. 'Nothing must happen to them – but first you must watch the performance. It's on in ten minutes.'

'I don't want Luigi working any more until he's fully recovered,' I said. 'Besides, he's infectious to anyone, including the public, with whom he might come into contact.'

The circus owner pulled the cork on a bottle of Montepulciano. 'Of course – whatever you say, *dottore*. Now, time for a *bicchiere* of good wine.' My kneecap throbbed relentlessly.

The show was second rate. Laddered fishnet, perished harness, bored clowns and an overwhelming sickly smell of popcorn. Then, to my astonishment, the curtains opened and an adult giraffe, urged on by an Arab with a stick, lurched drunkenly into the ring. Lame on a hind leg and plainly scared stiff, the giraffe reached the centre, raised its head to stare vertically upwards – a sign of stress in these animals – wheeled awkwardly on its bad limb and staggered as fast as it could out through the curtains, brushing the cursing Arab aside. My dismay at the spectacle turned to anger as, a moment later, a girl in a 'white hunter's' uniform of khaki bush-jacket and topi ran into the ring leading a loping Luigi on a neck collar and chain. To the blare of a scratchy recording of the *Trumpet Voluntary* she encouraged the gorilla to knuckle-walk all the way round the low wall of wooden blocks enclosing the ring. Luigi shuffled along listlessly flinging an arm at folk sitting in the front row and leaking a trickle of diarrhoea. Suddenly he jumped off the wall and dashed up a wooden gangway between the rows of seated spectators, dragging the white huntress behind him. Circus hands appeared from the shadows, Luigi's chain was seized by several pairs of hands and he was dragged away, half throttled, through a flap in the tent.

I went at once to find the Palmones. The old man and his son were in the horse lines getting things ready for the finale. '*Signori*, I said that Luigi should not work in the show!'

The young man gave me the crescent moon smile. 'But,

dottore, he no work. Just make an appearance, like you saw. That's all he does anyway, no work.'

'There's diarrhoea all round the ring and up the gangway! I told you — it's very infectious. And besides, he should rest until he's cured.'

Both men shrugged. '*Dottore*, you know how it is,' said the son. 'How you say? The show must go on.'

'Not if you expect me to help you,' I said. 'Don't you realize he's a valuable, precious, rare, endangered animal? He shouldn't be within a thousand miles of a circus.'

'But we look good after him, *dottore*. Give him the best. Not like those bloody darkies in Africa who *eat* gorillas. He's safe here.'

Lost for words, I marched off and stood in the twilight outside the tent watching the wind blow a snowstorm of wastepaper across the rubbish tip and listening to the gulls crying their laments over the darkening sea. Behind me in the big top a bass drum's steady beat heralded the start of the finale.

When the show was at last over and the costume and makeup had been removed, young Palmone took me to see the rest of the animals. The atmosphere between us was now distinctly strained. First we returned to the gorilla/ chimp wagon and after enduring the hullaballoo once more and waiting for Palmone to subdue it by dint of the iron tent peg, I inspected each of the chimpanzees. One by one the doors of the cages, except for the one holding an angry male, were opened by the circus man and I was able to see clearly the animal within. It was a prison visitor's tour of Death Row. Some of the chimpanzees sat solemnly at the back of their 'cells'. Others climbed warily out and descended to the floor of the corridor where they sat fidgeting nervously. I was stunned. Every one of them was afflicted by some disease or other. Here was one with a tooth abscess of long standing that had burst to leave a yawning chronic fistula in the lower jaw. There was one almost blind from double cataracts. A third had a tumour, the size of a goose egg on its scalp. Then another cage door was swung open and I came face to face with the sickest chimpanzee I had ever seen. A middle-aged female, she could neither walk nor climb nor even sit up, so weak was her condition. She could only squirm slowly on her belly. Her skin gleamed bone white through sparse black hair and her gums and conjunctivae were similarly blanched. She held my hand and snuggled up to me as I touched her emaciated form. Over each bony protruberance there was a bed sore forming.

'How long has she been like this?' I asked.

'Like what, *dottore?*'

I gritted my teeth and felt one of the crowns I'd just had fixed crumble into spiky fragments. 'Like – thin as a skeleton. White as a sheet. Weak as a mouse. Like that!' I shook a finger at him.

'Oh, Sara – she eats OK, *dottore*, she's just a little sleepy these days. I think she's getting old.'

'Bullshit, *signore*, BULLSHIT! She's not old, she's dying.' Trembling, I took my black bag off my shoulder and opened it. The emergency equipment inside – basic instruments, some special drugs, sample tubes and a selection of needles and syringes was all I had to work with. I decided to take a blood sample from Sara and have it analysed in England when I went home the next day. She didn't complain or resist as I took her arm and raised the vein for my needle. *Ex Africa semper aliquid novi*, I thought as I looked down at the blood I was drawing into my syringe. No opaque crimson fluid this, not even the watery Beaujolais Nouveau that I'd found in killer whales with severe blood loss. This was transparent *vin rosé* – for all the world more like the 'onion skin' wine of Provence than life-bearing blood. The haemoglobin level must be far below the critical level where transfusion is essential, I thought, as I pressed a swab to the puncture point. But what had caused so profound an anaemia? I laid Sara back on the floor of her cage and went over her carefully centimetre by centimetre. There was nothing to be found, at least not by my eyes or fingertips. No cancerous masses in the abdomen, no enlarged spleen or liver, no sign of blood loss via the rectum. I began to consider the possibility of a leukaemic or bone marrow malignancy. As a final exploration, I slipped on a rubber glove and inserted a finger into her rectum. Sara accepted the intrusion, a placid expression on her long, pale face. It was more difficult than usual entering the rectum. There was some resistance. I found my finger deflected to one side. A mass, outside the bowel wall, was impinging upon me. I put my other hand on Sara's pelvic region and pressed in. My finger in the rectum felt the pressure. Something big, something out of the ordinary, something tense but not hard, filled the pelvic cavity. I kneaded the skin of the perineum, between vulva and anus: there it was again, a well-defined swelling – fluid under pressure. I stood back and took off the glove. Anaesthesia of the chimp in this condition was too risky. Taking a scalpel from my bag, I fitted a new blade. 'Hold her firmly but gently,' I said to Palmone. He grasped her by the shoulders while I arranged her rear end to catch the best of the light from the grimy bulb in the ceiling. 'Hold tight, girl,' I whispered and stabbed the scalpel blade into the skin beside the anus. There was a gentle hiss as a jet of foul-smelling, lilac-coloured liquid erupted, narrowly missing me. I cut again to make the incision into a cross. I didn't want it healing too quickly. Sara seemed unaware of the knife. I pressed my fingers in around the opening and the liquid continued to flow vigorously. It was an enormous abscess in the pelvis that was at the bottom, literally, of Sara's troubles. After draining all the pus I gave the chimpanzee a large dose of long-acting amoxycillin and then considered the next step. If Sara had been a human, she would have been given a transfusion of at least two pints of blood, so anaemic was she. Why not do the same for her? I walked up and down the row of cages looking at the other chimpanzees – this mobile, living museum of primate pathology. Only the fierce-looking male appeared to be anything like healthy. He would have to be the blood donor.

Chimpanzees have blood groups similar, but not identical, to those of human beings. So do other mammals such as dogs, and birds have groups that are more complex than those of the majority of mammals. Even the humble farmyard chicken possesses at least eleven separate, inherited blood groups. Although matching the blood from donor and recipient is ideally to be desired, it is possible frequently to get away without matching if the transfusion is the first one ever to be administered to the recipient. Here on this Greek rubbish heap I had no way of accurately matching the chimpanzees' bloods. I decided to take a chance and began to assemble my short blowpipe. Half a teaspoonful of ketamine anaesthetic in a flying syringe, tip of blowpipe carefully positioned where the male chimp could not grab it, final check that I was out of his reach with my back against the outside wall of the corridor, filled my lungs with air and then 'poof', exhaled hard and fast down the mouthpiece. The syringe landed on target in the chimpanzee's upper arm. He howled with rage, snatched it out and chomped it between his teeth, but the pressurized plunger had already, in the twinkling of an eye, delivered the ketamine into his system. Three minutes later he was curled up, snoring peacefully, dead to the world.

Sara didn't need any such chemical control. I took her arm as she snuggled up to me, raised the vein and without any difficulty drew off a millilitre of the Mateus Rosé masquerading as blood. In a small tube I mixed Sara's sample of blood with one taken from the anaesthetized male and held it up to the light. Five minutes passed and there was no evidence, at least to the naked eye, that clumping of red blood cells or their destruction, both potential signs of incompatible samples, was taking place.

Time for the transfusion. I lifted Sara out of her cage and laid her down next to the male in his quarters. Debilitated as she was, she managed a whimper of apprehension when she found herself so close to the old bruiser, but she settled down at once after she watched me prod him firmly in the ribs to demonstrate that he was safely *hors de combat*. It must have puzzled her greatly that I didn't get my arm ripped off for my impudence. Without a system of plastic bags and tubing normally used for transfusions, I would have to improvise. There are always some large fifty milli-litres sterile syringes in my black bag – they would have to do. First I gave the male chimp a top-up injection of ketamine to prolong his 'coming out' from the anaesthetic, and then I placed a cannula in Sara's arm vein and taped it securely in place with Elastoplast.

Palmone held her arm steady while I concentrated on slowly drawing off fifty millilitres of blood from the male who I also cannulated. Once the syringe was full I connected it to Sara's cannula and very gently depressed the plunger. The blood would flow in faster than with a normal transfusion set-up. I had to watch for the first signs of any change in Sara that might indicate her body was reacting badly to the male's donation. One syringeful delivered, I began filling the next. Sara lay watching me patiently, occasionally blinking the livid eyelids over her large, chestnut-coloured eyes. It was a painfully slow business. My thumb began to ache from the application of steady measured pressure on the plunger. One hundred ml, a hundred and fifty ml, two hundred ml, two hundred and fifty ml. I decided that three hundred and fifty ml, around twelve fluid ounces, would be my aim – safe for the donor and hopefully enough to be really useful to the recipient. At long last, after almost one and a half hours and two 'toppings up' of anaesthetic for the male, it was done – and miraculously without either cannula blocking even once with clotting blood. Most pleasing of all was that Sara had not shown any unwelcome reaction to the transfusion and her face and gum were now distinctly less pallid. I put her back in her cage. With a bit of luck she would recover, I thought, but to what sort of future would she recover. I felt anything but elated by the apparent success I was having with her. Was it all to be, tragically, a waste of time? Prolonging a life of sadness and deprivation?

I had no time to reflect further. There were other patients – to wit all the other chimpanzees except the male. For the next two hours I knocked out the chimpanzees one by one and with scalpel, needles, forceps and scissors cut out lumps and dead tissue, extracted teeth, cleaned up ulcers and drained centres of chronic infection. There was nothing I could do for the blind chimp. A colleague, the eminent veterinary ophthalmic surgeon, Keith Barnett, with whom my partners and I have tackled many cataracts in exotic animals, from sealions to white tigers, was far away in Newmarket.

When there was nothing more I could do, and feeling exhausted for it was by now almost midnight, we left the chimpanzees and walked around the rest of the circus. There were still more unpleasant surprises in store for me. There were two giraffes in a pen the size of a billiard table – one, the animal I had seen during the performance, had clearly long been lame with hip disease, the other had a melon-sized swelling, possibly a cyst, on its rump. A rusty steel trailer contained a fully grown hippopotamus with skin disease and every one of the Liberty horses was coughing persistently and running at the nose. 'Equine flu,' I said. 'No, *dottore*, the dust from this damned rubbish tip,' replied Palmone. The lions all had coats broken by patches of ringworm, three clowns also carried typical ringworm lesions on their wrists and chests, and a bird that had once been a blue and gold macaw should probably have been reclassified as a nude macaw, having lost all his body and tail feathers. He sat shivering on a perch in the horse tent, an oven-ready but living bird with a squawking head that didn't seem to match his pink, translucent-skinned body. It was a small consolation to find that the footballing dogs looked to be fit as fiddles.

'That's the lot,' said Palmone as we concluded the tour of inspection. 'All of them part of our family. My papa's babies.' And so we walked back to his father's caravan to take dinner as they always did at around one in the morning, after which I was taken to my lodgings in the town.

The following morning both Luigi and Sara were looking much better and I concentrated on giving advice and prescribing treatment for the other animals. Ideally they needed a vet to travel with them permanently and he or she would certainly have found more than enough work in the circus to occupy their time. But that was a pipe dream, although I do recall a Cambridge graduate who saw practice with me as a student, spending a year or two travelling with Chipperfield's Circus and combining the role of resident vet with that of ringmaster. The best I could achieve under the circumstances was to advise and hope they would telephone me from time to time to report on progress or lack of it. It was very depressing.

After lunching on the pasta and *parmigiano*, the younger Palmone drove me back to Athens airport. Just before we parted he suddenly remembered something. 'Oh, *dottore*, I forgot to tell you. This afternoon we will receive some sealions at the circus.'

'You are hiring a sealion act?'

'No, buying the animals – from Benvenuti, the dealer in Italy. Three of them.'

'What kind of sealions?'

'I don't know.'

'Are they Californian or South American?'

'I don't know – except that I think they come from South Africa.'

South Africa meant South African fur seals. Delightful little creatures to look at, but mean biters and very difficult to handle. 'Who will take care of them in the circus?'

'My uncle Sandro and his wife Maria, the tightrope

walkers you saw last evening. They're getting too old and want to change to something less – you know – physical.'

'Have they any experience with sealions?'

'Oh no, *dottore*. They forgot to ask you while you were in Khalkis. How do you feed such animals? Do you need salt or sweet water for them? Things like that.'

My mind boggled. If a middle-aged circus couple wanted to go in for animals, dogs or doves or a comic donkey act were the sort of thing to think of. Not, above all *not*, fur seals. 'And where are they going to house the sealions?'

'Oh, Sandro is converting a van for them.'

'*Is* converting a van? Isn't it ready for them?'

'No. Maybe tomorrow, day after tomorrow. He wanted to ask you. How should he build the pool into the van for them?'

I looked up at the airport clock. The BA flight to London would leave in fifty minutes. '*Signore* Palmone,' I said slowly. 'Please, *please* tell your uncle that even thinking of sealions for his act is madness. It will all go wrong. Telephone Italy immediately and cancel, at least postpone, the animal shipment, I beg you.'

The Italian gave that big crescent smile again. 'But, *dottore*, is too late. The sealions are already in the air.'

As soon as he had left me I rushed through Passports and Security and went straight to the nearest telephone. In my bag I had a notebook containing the telephone numbers of a Greek animal protection society in Athens and the local office of CITES, the Convention on International Trade in Endangered Species. Just as my flight began boarding, I finished my calls. The wheels, hopefully, had been set in motion to save Luigi, Sara and the rest of the chimpanzees. Something might also be done to improve the lot of the other animals in Circo Coruña, as well as the fur seals that seemed set to join it very shortly. I wasn't under any illusions. Greece has not been noted in the past for its standards of animal welfare, but things have begun to improve since that country joined the European Community and members of the IZVG (International Zoo Veterinary Group) have been called to Greece several times in the past few years on matters concerning wild animals including escaped bears and monk seals in trouble. In the past both of the latter would simply have been shot without benefit of veterinarian.

As I half suspected I never heard from Circo Coruña again, but certain information did come my way. Two weeks after my visit arrived the bad news. Over a crackling telephone line from Cyprus I received a call in Richmond from a Cypriot vet with limited command of English. It seemed that an Italian circus had pulled into town with three sealions, animals he'd read about but never previously seen. One was dead and two were ill. Could I, please, tell him what the illness was? Had he done an autopsy? No. What symptoms were the living pair showing? He wasn't sure. They were ill. I told him to perform a post-mortem on the dead animal and then ring me back. He did. Two days later. Now a second animal had died. His findings at the first autopsy? Nothing. So what should he do? What indeed? I sometimes wonder whether some folk think I can run my practice by sitting in bed with a telephone nearby and just guessing diagnoses long distance. Or maybe there was real scope for a clairvoyant zoo vet. But I'd had my fill of clairvoyance with the Antoiniste nun and the killer whale in Antibes of which I have written elsewhere.

After thinking for a little while I said, 'Give an injection of tetracycline long-acting, some cortico-steroid and vitamin B complex. Without a diagnosis, or at least some symptoms, I can promise nothing – oh, and say your prayers to St Herman.'

'To who?'

'The orthodox saint who lived in Alaska. He must have seen any number of seals.'

'But how do I inject the sealion?' The line went dead and I never heard from him again.

The good news, the very good news, arrived six weeks later. After several violent confrontations, Luigi the gorilla, Sara and the other chimpanzees had been seized by the Greek authorities backed up by ample constabulary. The animals were in a temporary refuge while arrangements were being made to send them to the chimpanzee sanctuary, 'Monkey World', at Wareham in Dorset, England, where we act as veterinary consultants. I felt like dancing – Anthony Quinn in *Zorba the Greek*. Luigi was out! Sara and I would meet again!

4

Morocco Bound

Death was only five minutes away.

To the east, hour after hour, always to the east, the
crumpled bleached khaki fabric of the desert that stretched
unseen for over three thousand miles to the banks of the
Nile itself. Out there, marooned in the sand, lay the
legendary lost saltmine of Taghaza, the ancient lands of the
blue-clad Tuareg 'men of the blue veil', the Mountains of
the Aïr, the sand sea of Ténéré, dunes where the wind hisses
over the exposed bones of dinosaurs and the ancient routes
of the slaver caravans. To the west, a mere hundred yards
away, an abrupt change. The desert ended in a jagged cliff
line that dropped vertically to where the Atlantic rollers
broke with thunderous roars and the sunlight danced on an
ocean of polished gun-metal blue.

The crash of the great breakers, the unrelenting whistling
of the dust-laden north-easterly wind from the Sahara, the
harmattan, was suddenly punctuated by the growl of an
automobile engine. A gannet resting from its labours on the
cliff top turned its head as the sand-encrusted Land-Rover
skirted a low dune that had built up across the track. The
heavily laden vehicle moved on past the watching bird with
the faint sound of Elton John's 'Candle in the Wind' coming
from a cassette player. The gannet took to the air and rose
high on an updraught above the Land-Rover as it growled
slowly along parallel to the coastline. Then the bird wheeled

violently, its body bucking in a blast of fiery hot air, accompanied by a 'boom' louder, though briefer, than those announcing the assault of the great waves. A cloud of dense black smoke enveloped the Land-Rover. When it cleared, blown away rapidly by the wind, the vehicle was no more than a lunatic jumble of black metal. In and around the wreckage four men lay dead. A fifth had been blown through the air by the force of the explosion and now lay unconscious some yards away, bleeding and with both legs broken.

A hundred feet below the injured man in the roof of a pitch-dark cave, the explosion had loosened rocks, one of which had fallen and claimed another innocent victim. A young seal with a fractured skull, blood streaming from its nose, laboriously drew its final breath. The gannet, terrified, beat its wings furiously and headed out towards the horizon's silver line.

The most primitive of all species of seal, the first ones ever described (by Aristotle in the third century BC) and the rarest, are the monk seals. So called because their colouring, dark grey or brown above and pale beneath, somewhat resembles the Dominican friars' garb of a black mantle worn over a white habit. Monk seals exist, but only just, as two species – the Hawaiian monk seal and the Mediterranean monk seal. A third species, the Caribbean monk seal, has not been seen since 1952 and is almost certainly extinct. The Mediterranean monk seal was once commonly found in all parts of the Mediterranean, the Black Sea and in the Atlantic around Madeira, the Canaries and along the West African coast from Morocco down to Mauritania. Then, yes, you've guessed it, Man set about destroying it with a vengeance. Hunted for its skin, killed by fishermen for allegedly raiding their nets, its breeding places disturbed by the onward march of tourism, its food sources depleted by human overfishing, the number of monk seals dropped steadily. In the mid Seventies I remember them living in sea-washed caverns on the island of Cabrera, off Majorca, when I used to go looking for the equally rare indigo-coloured Lilliford's wall lizard there. The caverns are deserted now. A few linger in Greek and Turkish waters off the Aegean, still persecuted from time to time by fishermen. A handful live around Madeira. The biggest remaining population, however, is in the Atlantic – inhabiting a fairly short length of coastline at the edge of the Sahara about one thousand miles south of Casablanca in what was, and still is in some respects, a remote and forbidding part of the world. But even there, the numbers are declining. Their ancient, tranquil refuges are being violated; the seals have nowhere else to hide. And the invaders are not just Man and his Works. An equally dangerous new enemy is abroad – and it is invisible.

Over the past ten years conservationists have increasingly debated the Mediterranean monk seal – what is to be done about it? It is an international problem involving a host of countries which were or are the natural homelands of the seal and which are or purport to be concerned about its fate. Politics, big business, traditional industries and tourism are major players in the complex drama surrounding this gentle creature that has quietly fished its waters for the past fifteen million years. Graeco-Turkish rivalries in the eastern Mediterranean have hampered efforts even to count the surviving stock of animals. Seals have almost certainly been counted twice, once as 'Greeks' and again as 'Turks'. Overfishing of the sea – plain as a pikestaff to anyone dining in an Italian or Spanish restaurant on *chanquetes*, illegal but easily obtainable baby fish or tiny immature squid – continues apace. Nowadays the boats of the tourists and the toilets of their hotels foul the 'wine-dark sea', in places that were peaceful and unspoilt only a few years ago. The understandable but uncontrolled proliferation of effluent-producing factories, particularly in some developing countries, brings economic progress but with it comes a steady rise in heavy metal and other chemical levels in the ocean waters.

Some highly commendable rescues of individual monk seals have been achieved by groups in Greece and Spain, programmes to educate fishermen have begun in Greece and North Africa and habitat protection schemes introduced in the Greek Sporades. The outlook for the survival of the species as a whole, however, looks depressing. Some experts consider the population size – a world total now thought to be no more than two hundred – has dropped below the minimum essential to avoid extinction, and five years ago Sir Richard Harrison, a world authority on marine mammals, told me at a monk seal meeting we were both attending, 'quite frankly I suspect that the monk seal is a busted flush'.

Among the numerous groups concerned about the monk seal crisis was one convened by the French government and the National Park of Port-Cros at Hyères in Provence; and of which I was made a member as a result of my long association with the Marineland at Antibes. Unlike some other groups, however, the French one did move steadily towards a plan for positive action. It decided that the crucially important colony of monk seals on the coast of the Spanish Sahara would be surveyed with a view to establishing, if possible, a captive breeding group from which reintroduction into their old habitats could be conducted at some time in the future. I was not surprised that several environmentalist groups, those with the loudest voices and the least scientific backbone, reacted adversely to the French proposal. 'Scandalous to take the animals from their homes', 'Keep those creatures out of zoos', 'Exploitation of the poor creatures' – the critics thundered mindlessly. Sadly, they had neither studied the problem nor weighed the possible solutions. None had travelled to the Saharan coast to see for themselves the real situation of the seals. None had appreciated the various threats that loomed over the seals in their own last fastnesses. It was plain to me that some of the more fanatical and 'green' organizations opposed to the French initiative would prefer the disappearance of the monk seal forever rather than an attempt, albeit in (emotive word) 'captivity', to create a sanctuary for the creatures.

The difficulty of breeding monk seals in a zoo or marineland was never underestimated by us. Maybe we would fail. But it had been done successfully with other highly endangered species in such places as Jersey Zoo with the pink pigeons, Port Lympne Zoo with Przewalski's horses, San Diego Zoo with Californian condors, Phoenix and Al Ain Zoos with Arabian oryx and Woburn Wild Animal Park with Père David's deer. Just *maybe* we could do it in the big Marineland at Antibes on the Côte d'Azur. Better to try and fail than not to try at all.

Thus it came about that a brilliant young French biologist, Didier Marchessaux, who like me was a member of the French Comité Scientifique Internationale Pour La Sauvegarde du Phoque Moine, began his studies of the Atlantic coast population of Mediterranean monk seals. In the latter half of the 1980s Marchessaux surveyed the Saharan coast, found beaches and caves where the seals rested and gave birth, counted them, observed their daily lives, and even managed to take blood samples from them while they slept. On the sound basis of his research, the French committee would work out its plans for future action. One of the most important objectives of Marchessaux's research was to try to establish as accurate a number for the monk seal population as possible. Then it would be up to our committee to decide on how many animals, and of what sex and age, we could safely take to set up the breeding experiment, without damaging the social grouping and breeding potential of the remainder.

The principal area of interest for us lay along the Cap Blanc peninsula. It lies at the junction of the extreme southern limit of the old Spanish Sahara, the Rio de Oro, with Mauritania. The Moroccan government's annexation of the Spanish Sahara has been disputed by the Polisario guerrillas in a war that has flared fitfully for many years. Far below the long rampart of sand that the Moroccans set up as a sort of Berlin Wall or Maginot Line to keep out the Polisario guerrillas who claimed the land as theirs, it is a barren place where even nomads seldom travel. On what was to be his last visit to Cap Blanc in 1988 Didier Marchessaux and four companions travelled 200 miles overland by Land-Rover from Dakhla, the southernmost coastal town. The track down the desert was said to have been cleared of mines by the Moroccan army. After making a survey of all the likely monk seal caves in the target area, they set off back towards the north. The explosion that killed four of the five men was said at first to have been caused by a mine, but was later unofficially attributed to an anti-tank round fired by, who knows, Polisario or Moroccan soldiers. The sole, badly wounded survivor crawled for two days on hands and knees before being found by Mauritanian troops near Nouadhibou on the Mauritanian border. He had with him notes and film recording the finding of around a hundred and thirty monk seals living along a fourteen-kilometre stretch of the coast and making use of two and possibly four caves for sleeping, giving birth and rearing young.

Stunned by the loss of Marchessaux and his companions, one of whom, Alain Argiolas, had been the first-class aquarist at the Marineland in Antibes where I was consultant, the committee nevertheless decided that the monk seal project must be carried on. With the support of the French and Moroccan governments a new expedition was planned for autumn 1990. The approach this time would be from the sea and, after reconnoitring the caves, an attempt would be made if possible to capture six animals to set up the breeding group in Antibes.

Timing was the crucial factor. Only for a few days in the year, in spring and autumn, is the Atlantic ocean off Cap Blanc relatively calm. At other times the mouths of the

caves are constantly battered and submerged by waves that
have travelled thousands of miles from the west, finally to
clash with the edge of Africa. Despite the great breakers
that roar into the cave entrances every few seconds, the
seals deep inside their airy chambers haul out above the
waterline on sloping beaches of shingle. They move in and
out of their lairs by swimming underwater. We decided that
our best chances of entering the seal caves in fair weather
would occur in October and November. The advance party
would go early in October to try to establish which caves
the seals were using and, if their report was encouraging,
the main expedition, which I had been asked to lead, would
follow towards the end of the month.

Meanwhile, another potential threat to the survival of the
monk seal, and one that had concerned me since 1988,
came upon the scene. In that year an epidemic quite unlike
anything we had seen before swept through the seal
colonies of the North Sea coastal regions, killing some
eighteen thousand animals. Dead and dying common seals
were found in alarming number on the beaches of Great
Britain, the Netherlands and elsewhere. Initially, without
waiting for thorough scientific study of samples taken from
ill and dead animals to be completed, organizations such as
Greenpeace stridently proclaimed that the cause of the new
malady was the old enemy, pollution, and used the emotive
images of winsome baby seals to belabour governments and
industry yet again. It was certainly true, as we had found in
many but not all post-mortems of seals performed over the
previous fifteen years, that levels of such chemical com-
pounds as PCBs as well as mercury and cadmium were
significantly high. It had been shown that such pollutants,
in certain other species such as birds, weaken the body's
immune system and interfere with normal reproductive
processes. But I couldn't believe that these chemicals could
be the primary cause of such a sudden, rapid and
widespread mortality rate in the seals. The answer hadn't

been long in coming. Scientists in Holland and Northern Ireland found a virus in the affected animals and identified it, to everyone's surprise, as a bug closely related to that which causes distemper in dogs. What was more, dog distemper vaccines seemed likely to give protection against the virus if administered to seals. Where the morbillivirus, as it is called, came from in the first place is so far a mystery. It has been suggested that Arctic foxes with distemper may have transmitted the disease while attacking a young seal hauled out of the water somewhere on the Scandinavian coastline. On the other hand, maybe the virus had been living harmlessly in seals for donkeys' years and then, suddenly, as is often the case with viruses, mutated into a more dangerous form capable of causing overt disease.

The identification of the seal disease virus and the availability of canine distemper vaccines wasn't the solution to controlling, let alone eradicating the epidemic. A puppy is taken to the vet's surgery for its first distemper 'shot' when it is about two months of age and returns for its second, two to three weeks later. After that it receives an annual 'booster' injection. A single injection of vaccine given to a dog without the necessary follow-up injections would give immunity that lasted only a few weeks. How could a minimum of two distemper vaccine shots be given to wild marine animals? Delivering an injection to a seal on a beach or in some cases in the water, could be achieved by using the flying syringes and blowpipes that are standard equipment for a zoo vet. But identifying a seal and finding it again after some weeks. Hardly possible. Another problem: the type of vaccine to use. All modern canine distemper vaccines are composed of living but weakened virus particles, or rather, I should say, weakened by laboratory processing so that although they induce an immunity in dogs they do not cause symptoms of distemper to develop. But what would happen if the vaccine was used in other species such as seals? Previous experience with certain vaccines used in species other than those for which they were designed had been sometimes alarming. I remembered the late Sixties when live erysipelas vaccines weakened for use on pigs had been injected into dolphins in the USA (dolphins, like pigs, are prone to the potentially deadly erysipelas or 'diamond' disease). Some dolphins had subsequently developed erysipelas and died. Likewise some vaccines against feline enteritis in domestic cats had produced the disease when given to cheetahs.

Ever since I became responsible for the giant pandas (and also the lesser or red pandas) at Madrid Zoo, both species which are also susceptible, we believe, to canine distemper, I have regularly vaccinated the animals each year with a specially produced *dead* vaccine which I obtained from the USA. With the seals it was also decided not to risk living distemper vaccine and a Dutch pharmaceutical firm began to manufacture trial batches of dead vaccine. I tried out some of the first phials on grey and common seals in the Marineland at Antibes. The seals suffered no ill effects and, to my delight, showed good levels of protective distemper antibodies in their blood when sampled some weeks later. But the difficulty of vaccinating wild seals remains. Perhaps one day in the future an *oral* vaccine similar to the one recently developed for immunizing wild foxes against rabies – it is administered in tasty edible pellets scattered near fox holes – will be available for feeding in fish.

Although the seal epidemic had affected animals in northern Europe, there was by 1990 circumstantial evidence which suggested the virus might be travelling south and threatening Mediterranean animals. Another epidemic, this time in striped or blue-white dolphins, had exploded out of the blue – it also was caused by morbillivirus. Additionally, an unusually high number (six or seven instead of the annual average of two) monk seal corpses were being washed up on coasts bordering the Mediterranean. Too putrified when discovered to yield solid evidence of morbillivirus, the bloated corpses deeply worried those of us concerned about the monk seals. What if the virus was about to move even further south down the African coast? Could it not conceivably wipe out the Cap Blanc colony? The morbillivirus was a further reason for setting up the captive breeding programme if at all possible.

At the beginning of November 1990 I went with Michael Riddell, the Director of the Marineland in Antibes, and other members of the French committee, to Brussels to a meeting of scientists called by the EEC Scientific Commission to discuss the ends and methods of our proposed expedition. Apart from a very few dissenting voices who rather lamely suggested that the monk seals be left undisturbed and to the mercy of God, but were unable to suggest how the diverse threats to the colonies' existence could be combated in any other way that was both practical and speedy, there was an overwhelming consensus in favour of us attempting to catch two male and four female adult monk seals, and to inject as many of the other animals as we could with the Dutch vaccine. I would also take blood samples from captured seals for testing in Holland and Great Britain. More important, I declared that the operation would be carried out at all times humanely and described my criteria for conducting the expedition. If there were at any time signs of stress or risk of injury to the seals, we would stop at once. The welfare of the seals was our paramount concern and I had, and was prepared to use if necessary, an absolute veto, enabling me to abort the expedition at a moment's notice.

After the meeting Michael and I discussed final plans over a bowl of mussels in the Rue des Bouchers. My friend had, as usual, organized his end of the operation down to the last detail. A large pool of filtered water with a cave was ready at the Marineland to receive any monk seals we caught. An even bigger system of pools, beaches and caves would be completed by the time the animals came to France. Our intention to acclimatize the seals for a while in a pool in Morocco, gave abundant time for this to happen. It had long been agreed by all of us on the French committee that the monk seals would not be on public view when living in the Marineland. Their, hopefully, breeding group would be situated in a quiet spot and totally surrounded by high wooden boarding. Only essential staff, vets and scientists involved in the enterprise would ever come in contact with the monk seals. Contrary to the carping of some ill-informed animal liberationist groups, the Marineland monk seal project was far from being an opportunist and commercially lucrative publicity stunt. All of us were well aware of the difficulties that lay ahead. Little was known about the ways of these animals. Apart from Didier Marchessaux, no one had had any experience of contact with significant numbers of the creatures. Only a few rescued individuals had ever been in captivity, the most notable being a couple from Greek waters cared for by the excellent Seal Sanctuary at Pieterburen in Holland. Breeding had not occurred though this may well have been due to the animals being of the wrong sex or immature.

It wasn't at all clear how the monk seals would react to human contact. There were many reports of their nervousness. Years before a British photographer had described to me how he had swum into a pitch-black grotto used as a dormitory by monk seals on the island of Cabrera. Clad from head to toe in black frogman's gear he had entered the cave while all the seals were out at sea feeding, and had waited for hours in the chilly darkness in the hope of taking flash photographs when they returned, bellies full of fish. Unfortunately he had overlooked his luminous wristwatch. When at last the seals returned and hauled out on to the grotto's beach, the feeble glow of light was enough to panic them into diving back into the water *en masse* and racing down the watery tunnel that led to the sea. On the other hand, and I put more weight on his account, Marchessaux had vividly recounted how he had often taken blood samples from the rear flippers of seals snoozing on land. On one occasion while standing, legs apart, over the rump of a big male weighing perhaps 250 kilograms, needle already placed within a vein, the animal rolled slightly to one side trapping one of Marchessaux's shins hard against a boulder. Sleepily the seal turned its head towards Didier's leg and opened its large dark eyes. The long, sharp, pointed fang teeth were within inches of the biologist's kneecap. For a few long seconds the big male gazed at the man straddling him. Didier froze, tensed for the shock of a powerful bite. But then the animal's eyelids closed, it turned its large, round head away, rolled back into its original position, freeing the leg, and went back with a deep and contented sigh to its slumbers.

But one man approaching sleeping monk seals was quite a different matter from my plan of taking a group of ten or more men into one of the caves on Cap Blanc and somehow catching and loading six animals into specially built boxes. The nature of our reception by the animals was a matter of much speculation and all depended on the information brought back by the advance party. Michael had arranged for our team – three Frenchmen, two Moroccans, my old friend John Kershaw with whom I had been on several adventures with marine mammals and myself – to have at our disposal a Moroccan naval fisheries protection vessel, a party of Moroccan navy frogmen and a contingent of marines. We would take an inflatable Zodiac launch and outboard engine with us from France. A Moroccan fisheries scientific ship would meet us off Cap Blanc. The advance party would make contact with carpenters to build crates in Dakhla, the harbour town where we would join our ship. The Moroccan military had agreed to give us full cooperation, obtain meteorological forecasts and provide us with a disused swimming pool in an officers' mess for conversion into an acclimatization pool for the seals.

'Communications with Dakhla are virtually impossible,' Michael said as we finished our bowl of mussels in white wine. 'The telephone line through the desert up to Agadir rarely works.'

'So how are we going to keep in contact with you in France?' I asked.

Michael tapped his nose and gave a big wink. 'French secret service, you'll find out,' he said cryptically. 'But once you sail south to Cap Blanc it will be even more difficult. Your ship will only be able to relay the most urgent messages via their naval headquarters at Agadir.'

'And Dakhla, the town – is it a place where I'll be able to get any materials that turn out to be necessary – repairs and so on?'

'Dakhla,' Michael replied after some moments leaning back in his chair and looking up at the ceiling. 'Dakhla when it was in Spanish hands was called Villa Cisneros, the town of the swan catchers. Now the Arabs call it the end of the world. I was briefly clapped in jail there once. It's an absolutely appalling place.'

Some days later the reports from the advance party reached me now back in England and I had the first taste of what was to come. Roger de la Grandière, Said and Mohammed had on two occasions visited the monk seal caves. On the first the sea had been calm but the animals had been 'very nervous' and it was impossible to take a Zodiac into the caves. The second visit was described by the Moroccan navy divers as 'a suicide mission'. They had entered a cave mouth carried in by a wave which then broke over the beach deep within the cavern. They counted about twenty animals resting there, many of which promptly dashed off into the water even though the men stayed at a distance. Getting out had been tricky and had to be done in the brief interval between successive incoming waves. Mohammed, a burly cheerful marine biologist who had just been married, was however very optimistic. 'Inshallah, we shall catch those seals in no time at all,' he assured me. But he'd never handled any kind of seal previously. Sure, those big eyes set in gentle faces give the impression of a cuddly creature – particularly the youngsters, and smaller species such as the

common, or harbour, seal of the North Atlantic and the
North Pacific. Not so – they inflict deep, tearing, often
serious bites that tend easily to become septic. More
worrying, however, were the apparent hazards of working
inside the caves. I didn't want Mohammed's bride to be
quickly widowed in the cause of monk seal conservation.
There were so many imponderables in what would be a
complex and delicate operation working far from civiliza-
tion and with capture methods that had never been tested in
practice. But the biggest question mark hung over the sea
conditions at Cap Blanc. What if the weather changed while
we were inside the caves?

My exhilaration was tinged with foreboding as I flew
down to Casablanca to set the expedition in motion. On the
plane I was seated next to a tipsy Dutchman who
harangued me throughout the flight concerning his dislike
of Belgians. 'Only two men of note ever came from
Belgium,' he kept muttering in my ear. 'The inventor of the
saxophone and the painter Rubens. But at least he made
love to his wife a few minutes before dying. Imagine a
Belgian doing that.'

In Casablanca I met up with John Kershaw and Philippe
Robert. John, one of the most experienced marine mammal
men in Europe, a powerful swimmer in perfect physical
condition, had worked with me in England, Spain and
finally France for almost twenty years. Philippe was a
biologist from the National Park at Port-Cros, a charming
and enthusiastic young Frenchman whom I had not met
before. The next day we were joined by Roger de la
Grandière, a rather eccentric ginger-haired French buc-
caneer in his forties with long experience of the sea and the
creatures that live in it, Pierre Escoubet, the dark-bearded
ichthyologist and aquarist from the Marineland, Said, a
zoologist from Rabat, who among other things had
extensively studied the wild cats of the Atlas mountains,
and finally Mohammed, our link with the Moroccan
Ministry of Fisheries.

Roger confirmed what Didier Marchessaux had described on his several visits to Cap Blanc. The civil war had taken its toll on the seal habitat. Open beaches where they used to bask were deserted, littered with the rusting detritus of battle. Explosives had caused some cave roofs to collapse and though a truce had been in force for some time and was generally holding, scouting military vehicles and mine clearance work continued to disrupt the solitude. 'And what is more,' Roger continued, 'I climbed up the rocks through a hole in the roof of one empty cave where once Marchessaux recorded over thirty mothers and babies hauled out and, *merde*, when I emerged on the desert sand there was a loaded missile launcher aimed towards the north, Cyrillic markings on the metal and plastered with faded photographs of Colonel Gadaffi.'

'Was there anyone about?' I asked, uneasy at the prospect of running into any of the colonel's cohorts.

'No one on land that I could see, but there were several Russian trawlers close inshore watching me constantly through binoculars. Oh, by the way, I've arranged with the commandant of the garrison at Dakhla to give us protection when we go to Cap Blanc. He's going to put an arc of paratroopers on the desert above the caves.'

'But I thought the civil war was over, or at least a truce in force?'

'It is.'

'Well, is it safe to take the expedition?'

'*Absolument!*'

'Why the paratroopers then?'

Roger grinned, sucked on his cigarette and gave a classic Gallic shrug of the shoulders. 'As you Anglo-Saxons say — it's Indian country down there!'

Over steaming bowls of tasteless tajine and couscous we discussed matters and I divided responsibilities. Roger in charge of the logistics and negotiations with officials; Philip, the Zodiac and the pool at Dakhla; John, head of the group that would try to enter the cave; Said and Mohammed, animal attendants; and myself as veterinarian and overall leader. The method of catching the seals was thoroughly thrashed out, but only in theory of course. Flying darts full of tranquillizers were out – doped animals in water can easily inhale water and drown. Basically we decided to use a low wall of wooden boards, hinged every two feet or so with rope ties. Folded up, this contraption would be taken towards the caves in the Zodiac and then floated on inflated rubber inner tubes through the entrance and down the passageway to the seal beach by teams of swimmers in wet suits. Arrived at the beach, they would quickly emerge from the water, erect the wooden wall around the seals and hold it in place with steel rods thrust into the gravel. Another Zodiac provided by the navy and carrying a transport box would arrive immediately and then a third, bringing up the rear and bearing me and my drug box. Under the light of torches I would peer over the wall and select suitable animals for the 'catch'. A gap in the surround of boards would then be opened and, one by one, the seals allowed to escape into the water – after I'd jabbed them with morbillivirus vaccine. When one of the selected animals was ready to go, the transport box would be put in place to block the gap and hopefully the seal would scoot through into it and the slide door would be dropped behind it. The crated seal would then be ferried back to the ship by Zodiac and another empty box brought to the cave on the dinghy's return. It *sounded* fine – such methods worked well with lots of animals including seals *on beaches* – but nobody had ever tried it with monk seals in caves. And although it was difficult to believe it might work, I couldn't come up with anything better.

Early next morning we loaded the Zodiac and all the rest of our gear and boarded one of the twice-weekly flights that served the outpost of Dakhla one thousand miles to the southwest.

Dakhla is a garrison town of a few thousand inhabitants

that serves as the principal rest and recreation fleshpot for Moroccan troops on leave from service in the Sahara. But this dusty, wind-harried place is no Saigon or Subic Bay. It has more of the air of one of those Mexican pueblos in a Clint Eastwood western. There is one hotel, rather appropriately called 'The Doums', one derelict Catholic church and one grimy little bar run by the only Spaniard left in town. It serves nothing but cans of warm Heineken and bottles of impressively foul wine, legally to infidel visitors of which there are virtually none, and illegally, wrapped in paper for consumption off the premises, to soldiers of which there is a steady furtive stream. Most houses are small, dirty-white brick hovels, some with little yards. The words in Arabic scrawled on the doors of some houses say 'this is a respectable home'. The majority of the dwellings do not bear this inscription, for Dakhla is, not surprisingly, one large and noisome brothel.

My team and I took rooms at The Doums which had a telephone line over which, the owner informed me, it was possible to talk to Casablanca – provided about two days' notice was given. The stench from the sewage, the grim food and the heavy air of gloom about the place quickly drove us out, and next day we moved to rooms at the officers' barracks, a courtyarded building which had seen better days, set on the water's edge. If anything, the sewage stench was more intense, but the food was better and there were showers that worked occasionally. The free entertainment at mealtimes was provided by the flies who fed greedily on saucers filled with yellow granules of some substance that were placed on the tables and every other flat surface. In death throes that lasted throughout our repast, the flies proceeded to perform strenuous bizarre dance patterns, jigs, pasodobles and eightsome reels – a formidable entomological corps de ballet whose terminal jetés always landed precisely in the middle of my next forkful.

On our first morning in Dakhla John, Roger and I inspected the preparations for our voyage to Cap Blanc, the

capture equipment and the facilities for holding any seals
caught during acclimatization. Nothing pleased me except
the ship, the *El Hamiss*, that lay at anchor in the harbour. A
newly built corvette still without its guns, it had only been
in service for a few months. The captain was a tall
charming man who spoke excellent English and his crew
were smart and appeared to be briskly efficient. The party
of marines and navy divers were already on board, the
latter checking their scuba gear, filling air tanks and
securing three more inflatable dinghies on deck. The captain
informed me that he was ready to set sail.

Unfortunately, the empty swimming pool at the officers'
barracks didn't suit me at all. Its filtration didn't work and
its bottom was covered with caked dirt and rubbish. An
alternative acclimatization pool for the monk seals was a
small sea inlet on the beach which could be netted off to
form an enclosure. However, further inspection provided
plain evidence of sewage contamination in the water. That
wouldn't do either. With the captain of the *El Hamiss* keen
to raise anchor while the weather forecast for the coast to
the south was good, I decided that if we caught any seals,
we would airlift them to the Côte d'Azur immediately and
acclimatize them in their new home. It would be safer. The
crates that had been built by local carpenters were another
disappointment. John climbed up on top of one and his foot
promptly broke through the flimsy roof. Nail points
protruded through the thin, unseasoned wood. Some of the
wooden slats that formed the floors of the crates were
broken. Wire mesh and ventilation panels were corroded in
places. Hardly robust enough boxes for animals that can
weigh up to three hundred kilograms. Yet despite their
flimsiness they were at the same time very heavy – how
would we get them into the monk seals' grottos without
overturning the Zodiacs, and once inside, manoeuvre them
into position without so much manpower that the seals
might panic and escape? It was not an auspicious start to
our venture.

'We'll have to modify the crates on board the ship while we go south,' I told my companions. 'John, Said and Mohammed – scour the town for wooden panels, screws and rope. I need to speak to Michael in France.'

This was where Roger came in, for even the military commander in Dakhla confirmed that he hadn't got a telephone line that could reach anywhere further away than Casablanca. It was time to enlist the help of the French secret services, as Michael had promised.

Roger had made contact with the French couple during earlier reconnaissance visits to Dakhla. Ostensibly running a tourist agency in this unlovely place, separated by one thousand miles of guerrilla-infested desert from Casablanca, and with The Doums hotel as the best, the only, accommodation around, the man was in fact, as Roger explained, a major and his wife a lieutenant, in the DGSE, successor to the old Deuxième Bureau. 'What is more,' Roger said as we walked along the beach on the outskirts of the town towards a large, red-painted house surrounded by a high wall, 'theirs is the only place in this *ville* where one can find a decent drink.'

And so it proved; we were soon sitting in a comfortable lounge sipping Bloody Marys and exchanging pleasantries before raising the matter of sending a message to the Marineland at Antibes.

'*Pas de problème, mes amis*,' replied the 'tourist agent' who could hardly have been described as being under 'deep cover'. 'Fax or voice, code or clear?' I wrote out a fax and our host disappeared into another part of the house with it.

'Satellite telephone link,' Roger whispered.

'It's gone – when there's a reply I'll drop it off at the harbour for you,' said the Frenchman when he returned after a few minutes.

Two hours later as the rest of our team returned to the *El Hamiss* with their purchases – wood and screws had turned out to be as scarce as gold nuggets in this desert outpost – the secret service agent duly turned up with a reply from

Michael in France. He was sending the head of his maintenance department and a couple of skilled joiners to Casablanca on the next flight from Marseilles. They would meet us on our return from Cap Blanc.

On board I was surprised to find a group of about twenty Moroccan marines carrying hand weapons crammed into a mess below decks. 'What are the guns for?' I asked the captain.

He shrugged, turned the palms of his hands outward and smiled broadly. 'Well, just . . .' He didn't finish the sentence but turned to go up to the bridge.

'I thought we were going down to a *pacified* area of the Sahara,' I said quickly.

'But we are,' he said looking back at me. 'It's the far south of Morocco and there's absolutely no trouble down there.'

'Why the marines then? We won't be going on to the desert, just into the caves at the cliff bottom where it meets the sea.'

The captain smiled an even broader smiler and began to climb the companionway. 'Doctor, we'll be casting off in twenty minutes,' he said. 'I think the army doctor would like to speak to you. He's in the ward-room.'

The army medic, a short pock-faced young man in battledress with red epaulettes shook my hand and introduced himself as Captain Mansur. 'I have been ordered to come along,' he said, 'although I'm not fond of sailing. *Eh bien*, what sort of special medical problems do you think we might face?'

'From my point of view the main risk, apart from the possibility of general injuries when going in by boat or swimming into rocky caves, will be bites from seals. You have a full medical kit?'

'A first-aid box. Dressings and so forth.'

'Antibiotics?'

'Antibiotics, no. You would require penicillin for any animal bites?'

Seals and sealions inflict nasty bites, dangerous not only because of the size of their canine teeth and the power of their jaws, but also because their mouths are commonly contaminated with a variety of unpleasant bacteria, most of them resistant to penicillin, and including one kind that can produce an extremely unpleasant infection called erysipeloid – known as 'blubber finger' or 'seal hand' to the seal hunters and whalers of days gone by. Following a bite or even just contact between an insignificant abrasion on human skin and the flesh of a skinned seal, inflammation accompanied by acute pain would develop. And there are stories of men in such unbearable agony that they chopped off their finger or hand with a cleaver in order to gain relative relief. For 'seal finger' the antibiotic of choice is tetracycline – and I always carry some in my black bag. I had enough for a course for three or four people.

'You'll need to carry tetracycline tablets,' I told the doctor. After asking the captain to wait a little while longer he dashed off the ship and jumped in a car to drive to the army hospital. Half an hour later he was back and showed me a tube of twenty-four tablets, all the tetracycline available in Dakhla. He had enough to treat one injured man.

The voyage to Cap Blanc took eighteen hours. As we sailed south along the Saharan coastline, the extent of the overfishing of the monk seals' natural hunting grounds became all too evident as vessels by the score of several nationalities – Russian, Japanese, Korean, Spanish, as well as Moroccan and a few Mauritanian – stretched towards the horizon like an unbroken palisade of shipping. The majority of boats worked outside the twelve-mile limit during the day but at night under cover of darkness, it got worse. I stood on the bridge and watched the miriad pinpoints of light on the radar screen, each of which represented a fishing vessel, as they blatantly broke the rules and moved towards land. The *El Hamiss* dashed about like a Jack Russell terrier in a warren of rabbits, sometimes launching a Zodiac carrying a couple of officers to race over and remonstrate with an intruder; but little was achieved.

The first – and early – casualty of the expedition was the doctor. He became violently seasick one hour out and staggered to me for treatment. The Stugeron tablets, which were keeping my stomach and John's perfectly calm, don't work when taken after nausea has developed, so Doctor Mansur retired to his bunk and was not seen again for the rest of the expedition.

We arrived at Cap Blanc at sunrise with a clear sky, a gentle breeze, a smooth long swell on the sea and the low tide we needed to expose the cave entrances. Two miles away we could see the cliffs that formed at the edge of the Sahara, an even line of pale rock almost one hundred feet high, crowned beyond with sinuous dunes. Everything looked fine for a run inshore on a Zodiac for a closer look at the seal caves. The captain gave orders that brought the ship closer to land and when we were a mile off he turned the stern of the vessel towards the cliffs. Much to my surprise the Moroccan marines then emerged at the double from below decks with Kalashnikovs and a Second World War heavy machine-gun which they set up on a tractor tyre lashed to the afterdeck.

'No photographing!' came the stern order from the bridge as members of my expedition brought out their cameras and the marines trained the barrel of their gun towards the desert.

'But I thought there was now no trouble with the Polisario down here,' I said yet again, to no one in particular.

'No, sir, there's no trouble at all,' answered a marine lieutenant standing nearby. 'No trouble at all in Morocco.'

At that moment I saw my first monk seals outside the Aegean and the Seal Sanctuary in Holland. Two charcoal-grey heads with even darker eyes had popped up out of the indigo water alongside the *El Hamiss* and were quietly inspecting us. From somewhere further forward an unseen person on deck threw the remains of a partly eaten sandwich overboard. To my astonishment one of the seals swam quickly over to the scrap of floating bread and gobbled it down. I heard the Moroccan sailor laugh and saw some grapes fly through the air. Before they could sink, the other seal sped in like an arrow and swallowed them.

'The Russians and the Koreans are taking all the fish, and these poor sods are having to fill up on scraps.' John had come over to watch the rare animals as they swam ever closer.

When the ramp doors of the stern of the corvette began to open with a loud grinding sound, the monk seals dived suddenly and vanished from view. Moments later the ship's big Zodiac with a powerful inboard motor slid down into the water and roared away carrying a quartet of navy divers in black scuba gear. I noticed one had a machine-pistol in his belt. John and I went up on to the top deck and watched through binoculars as the Zodiac approached the shore. We noticed how it regularly disappeared from view as if submerging and then reappeared. Though the sea surface was flat and oil-smooth where we lay with engines stopped, closer to the cliffs it was undulating with the Atlantic rollers at last heading for their final resting place. Then John gave a gasp and poked me in the ribs with a hard finger. 'Look at bloody that!' he exclaimed. 'Are those waves or what?' He pointed to the area of the cliffs where the caves were situated. 'Keep your eyes trained on there!'

I moved my binoculars from following the Zodiac and refocused on the place John had indicated. After waiting ten seconds I saw it. A plume of white sprang up from where the sea and the cliff merged, rising vertically until it was above the level of the desert. Then it blossomed briefly like a bunch of lilies before fading into invisibility. It wasn't long before the divers came bouncing back across the water and the ship swallowed up their rubber craft, the steel doors clanging shut behind it. John and I went below to talk to them.

'Impossible! Suicide! No way you can get in the cave. Or if you did get in, you'd never get out,' said the chief diver as he stripped off his gear. 'The waves are breaking on the cliff like demons. It may look like a millpond here, but when you get close inshore it turns into a white hell.'

I called my team together to discuss the situation. Roger and Mohammed were willing to try to swim through the breakers into the caves. 'Not if the navy divers think it's madness,' I ruled. There was nothing to be done except wait for the sea to halt its attack on the shoreline. In the cramped ward-room we had a meal of boiled sheep's heads, during which the eyeballs – delicacies! – were given to John for it was his birthday, and I ate my portion of eyelids, ears and nostrils, well doused in Tabasco, a condiment I always carry on such travels. Then we continued work on improving the seal crates, checking the gear and planning our tactics while waiting for conditions to improve. They didn't.

Nightfall came with the breakers still exploding against the cliff. 'The main difficulty is the *météo* – the weather forecast for this region,' the captain said as we sat in his cabin watching one Lisa Stansfield video after another. He was an ardent fan of the pop singer and had become ecstatic when I happened to mention that she was, like me, a Rochdalian. 'The forecast in Dakhla for Cap Blanc is eighteen hours out of date by the time we get down here – and anyway the information pays no attention to inshore sea conditions. No way of obtaining it.'

That was the nub of the problem – good weather could still mean the presence of awesome breakers. With time on our hands we discussed *ad nauseam* the problems facing us even if the waves did subside. I didn't sleep well that night.

Next day dawned bright and sunny again, the ocean, like the previous day, smooth and gently rolling. To my disappointment, however, the waves were still shooting high above the clifftops and further reconnaissance trips in the Zodiac throughout the day showed the cave mouths to be covered for all but a few seconds with raging floods of white water. All seemed quiet on the desert edge as the marines sat on the deck beside the machine-gun, smoking. The fishing lines we had put out over the side attracted not a single bite. No more monk seals came by our ship and on the horizon the line of trawlers, drift netters and factory ships looked like a blockading armada. 'But I reckon we might get into the cave,' Mohammed murmured from time to time as he leaned on a windlass staring towards the shore.

'And I know we'd bring you back in a bodybag,' grunted a nearby navy diver.

The third day off Cap Blanc with still no change in the weather or state of the sea. High tide, low tide or in between, the huge waves persisted. I made up my mind. 'Let's return to Dakhla,' I said to the captain. 'Now that I've seen the problems we face, I want to build better and lighter crates, reorganize the equipment and do some practising with the expedition members. With any luck, we'll try to come back here in ten days' time.'

And so the *El Hamiss* started up her engines and turned towards the north.

Five days later I was back in France for meetings with Michael who had arranged for his men in Casablanca to build the new stronger crates and other pieces of equipment. Then I moved on to Brussels to talk again with the EEC Scientific Committee where they approved my outlines for a second attempt to catch the six animals.

At the end of the first week of November I picked up the rest of my team in Casablanca and travelled once more to Dakhla only to find that the telephone line had suffered one of its frequent attacks of paralysis. No calls, no faxes had come in to warn the military or naval authorities to expect us. The *El Hamiss* was out at sea chasing trawlers and the garrison commander seemed far less pleased to see us than previously. It took hours of patient diplomacy by Roger, backed up by faxes from Michael sent to us via the secret service couple, whose lines of communication never failed, before good relations were restored. The clincher was news that His Majesty, King Hassan, was taking a personal interest in the success of the operation to save part of the Moroccan national heritage.

Nevertheless we would have to wait for two days for the arrival of the *El Hamiss*. I used the time to rehearse my team in the handling of the new crates and wooden catching-panels which had arrived from Casablanca by truck.

I formed two teams from the navy frogmen, marines and members of my group. In the shallow waters off a beach in Dakhla harbour they practised unloading a seal crate from a Zodiac, with me inside the crate acting as a proxy monk seal bull. Before any jokes about the appropriateness of my girth began, I pointed out that male monk seals weigh a good deal *less* than females. The teams rehearsed the manoeuvres with the wooden boards they would use to surround the seals, while I sat by with a stopwatch. It rapidly drained the energy of some of the strongest professional divers, and it would have to be done quickly and quietly, if we were to have any chance of success.

Between the rehearsals John and I explored the small town and took mint tea in one or other of the flyblown little cafés. Dakhla stands on a broad spit of sand with the sea on two sides. Attempting to reach the sea on the opposite side of the town from the harbour we found ourselves walking across a vast rubbish heap several hundred acres in area, which served also as a grand and very public convenience, housing estate and industrial enterprise zone. The strong wind off the ocean conjured up sand devils that spun across fields of broken glass, plastic and metal fragments. Here we came across men scavenging among the detritus, there a small compound walled by rusty tins enclosed a group of goats. Dwellings constructed of old tyres stood in gardens of smashed pottery. Nearer the sea a man in the blue rags of the once fearsome Tuaregs peered suspiciously from a hut composed of nothing but cracked chamber pots. Everywhere squatted folk using this graveyard of human artefacts for the purpose of relieving themselves. Anyone walking was either proceeding to or from the town before or after using the vast field as a communal 'al fresco' lavatory.

'We'd better watch how we go,' said John as we skirted yet another hillock of dazzling white bones and came upon a man crouched out of the wind in a cloud of flies. With an admirable lack of embarrassment at our arrival he carried on emitting a series of colonic rumblings both loud and plangent.

It took us three-quarters of an hour to cross the rubbish tip and at last reach the beach proper, a thin strip of dirty sand surely soon to be overrun by the derelict prairie behind it. Suddenly John grabbed my arm and pulled me hard so that I fell backwards behind a knoll of sand that had formed around the skeleton of some kind of motor vehicle. 'Did you see that?' he asked, mouth open, eyes wide.

'What?' I inquired, and my friend curled a finger and gestured in the direction of the beach beyond the knoll.

'A bunch of women lifting up their gowns, djellabahs, whatever you call them, with tubes up their bums.'

'*What?*'

'No, seriously – have a look – carefully, better not let them see we've spotted 'em.'

I remembered the pool near Ain Al Faydah in Abu Dhabi, reserved for women only who bathed without undressing, and which I'd been shown years before by the bird curator at the zoo in Al Ain when we were out looking for houbara bustards. Although no women had been in the pool at the time, it was prohibited for men, other than the sheikhs, even to see it, and unpleasant penalties were decreed for those who intruded upon the secret place. I didn't want for a second time to risk the accusation of being an infidel peeping Tom in this godforsaken place, but it was the tubes that intrigued me. Very cautiously I poked enough of my head around the edge of the heap of sand to use one eye. A hundred yards away a small cluster of middle-aged Arab women were sitting on the sand, or rather all but two of them were. They had obviously not seen us and were busily talking and ministering to the two women who lay among them, not squatting on their haunches like the others, but sprawled prone with their robes hauled up to their waists. Just as John had said, each of the two women had a tube seemingly of rubber, sprouting from their backsides and topped by a metal funnel which was held by one of her companions and into which was being poured some sort of clear liquid. I pulled my head back and stared at John. 'Good Lord!' I exclaimed. 'What on earth is all that about?'

'Beats me. Maybe it's the local version of a Tupperware party.'

'Or two poor ladies whose guts are obstructed by a surfeit of sheep's eyeballs! Anyway we'd better clear off before we're seen, I think.' We crawled away for a little distance until we could stand without risk of being seen and walked back marvelling towards the town.

That evening we described what we had seen to our Moroccan friends. Both laughed nodding their heads. 'What you saw is not uncommon around here,' said Said. 'Have you noticed how many plump women there are in the town?'

It was certainly true that there were lots of Junoesque ladies to be seen in Dakhla and the prostitutes, who after dark didn't so much strut their stuff at the doors of their hovels as waddle it about, were decidedly fat. 'Saharan men of this region like their women to be obese. And the women believe that to put on weight it is beneficial, as well as eating lots of couscous, to have oil – olive or peanut oil – introduced into their rectum. Eating at both ends they call it,' said Mohammed.

*

The *El Hamiss* was late in coming back to port. Another day of cave-entering rehearsals and mint teas passed slowly. In the cool twilight John and I walked through the alleyways where sellers of kebabed lamb and fish in spicy sauce to the ubiquitous soldiers were fanning their glowing charcoal in doorways, and the muezzin wailed his fourth call of the day from the rooftop of some unseen mosque. No sensuous domes or minarets in Dakhla.

'I must get a present while I'm here for X,' John named one of the staff at the Marineland whose birthday it would soon be. 'He's a great chap – as you know he's gay, but rather down at the mouth lately. Can't find a really nice boyfriend to suit him. Rather fastidious taste. Abhors one-night stands and the like. We must find something to cheer him up.' He wagged a finger at me. 'And no cheap retorts about "a Moroccan sailor perhaps", if you please.'

As John spoke we turned a corner and found ourselves beside the open doorway of a shop whose interior was lit, though barely, by the anaemic glow of a single electric bulb heavily freckled with fly droppings. There was sufficient illumination, however, for us to distinguish in the soupy gloom along the walls and heaped upon the counter, a host of wonderful shapes and smouldering colours. Our nostrils drew in a veritable gallimaufry of odours. Ginger, durian, sulphur, camel's milk, peppers, frankincense, dried fish, pine resin, billygoat and bladderwrack, all mingled yet individually distinguishable. We went in. Here were crocodile heads, boxes of dried spices, crystals of bright blue copper sulphate, sea shells of every imaginable variety, ropes fashioned of dried camel penises, phials of sinister dark red liquid, stuffed bats, and mortars brimming with black, white, yellow and green powders. A soft cough, and out of the shadows moved the owner of the establishment, a dark-skinned man with a beard but no moustache wearing a Harlem Globetrotters T-shirt. '*Messieurs*, how can I serve you?'

We were in a desert pharmacy, a herbalist, a Saharan

Olde Curiosity Shoppe, a sorcerer's cave. John instantly saw this as a possible answer to his quest for a present for X. 'We are looking for a love potion, a philtre . . . for a friend of ours.'

'You wish to make her want you, *monsieur*? What is her name?'

John turned to me. 'How do I explain it's for a feller?'

'Change the name of X to its feminine equivalent by adding the appropriate letter,' I replied.

'We . . . I need a love potion for a girl called X.' He added the correct feminine ending.

'I see. Yes, I can do it.' The shopkeeper screwed up his face like a squeezed handful of chamois leather. 'But I will need a whole day to prepare it. Can you come back tomorrow?'

'Yes – how much will it cost?'

'One thousand dirhams, *monsieur* – for most sure results. She will throw herself at your feet.'

'Three hundred dirhams is all I can afford.'

'*Monsieur* – the ingredients are rare and thus expensive.'

'Three hundred and fifty dirhams.'

'Four hundred dirhams, *monsieur*, and she will be yours within a fortnight.'

'Done!'

The next day we returned to the shop. The potion wrapped in brown paper was waiting for us. John paid the four hundred dirhams and asked for instructions as to the use of the preparation.

'Listen carefully, *monsieur*,' said the old man. A fat grey gecko ran out of the shadows of a dusty bottle, hopped and then climbed steadily up the apothecary's robe until it reached a shoulder where it sprawled staring towards us. 'This amatory powder will compel, insist, demand that she looks at you with the gazelle's eyes of love, with the soft gaze of a houri.'

'Houri?' said John. 'What's that? A whore? Doesn't sound quite what we . . .'

'Houri,' I whispered. 'A beautiful maiden who lives in paradise.'

'She will be enchanted by you,' continued the potion maker. 'But *you* must use it, not her. Each night while you sleep you must have a burner of charcoal by your bed. Sprinkle a pinch of my powder on to the hot charcoal before you close your eyes and the smoke produced will envelop your body during the night. Do this steadfastly every night for ten nights and then, then *monsieur*, go to see the chosen one. She will succumb instantly.'

'What's in the powder to make him, er, me whiff so potently?'

'Ah, *monsieur*, that I cannot divulge. So many things, so much work, so . . .'

'I understand, but is it mainly herbs or what?'

'*Monsieur*, it is a most unusual mélange. I cannot describe the complexities of its compounding. But . . .' he lowered his voice to a conspiratorial whisper '. . . I can tell you that there is whale foreskin employed in the making.'

'Like the bar stool in Onassis's yacht,' I said.

John gave me a funny look. He took the packet of powder, bade the apothecary 'adieu' and we left the shop.

'What was that about Onassis?' John asked me as we made our way to a nearby mint-tea seller.

'Oh, it was the mention of whales' foreskin. The only other time I've come across a mention of that fabulous prepuce was a couple of years ago in the *Spectator*. Someone wrote that the bar stools in Onassis's floating palace were covered in leather made from the foreskins of whales. As you and I both know, whales don't possess such things.' Which led us on to musing over the tea about the church in Italy that claims to have in a golden reliquary on the high altar Our Lord's foreskin, thoughtfully saved and put by by someone attending His circumcision. We debated whether the dried scrap of skin shouldn't have been resurrected along with the rest of the Holy Body some thirty-odd years later.

The elephant is one of my favourite patients. *(Roger Dixon)*

Luigi. *(J M Martos)*

Another successful gorilla birth at Madrid Zoo. *(J M Martos)*

Inspecting a robust Lesser (Red) Panda cub at Madrid Zoo. *(David Taylor)*

Chang-Chang the Giant Panda undergoes one of his regular medical check-ups. *(J M Martos)*

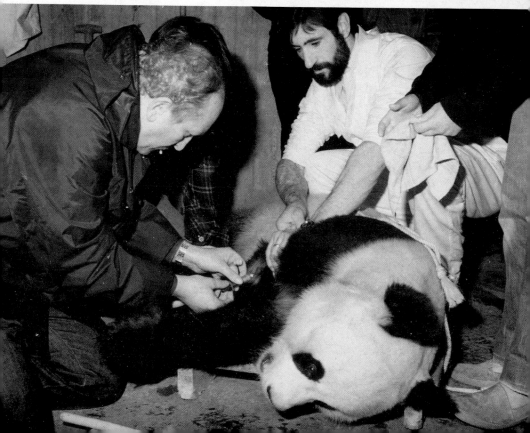

Chu-Lin, the Giant Panda bred at Madrid Zoo. *(David Taylor)*

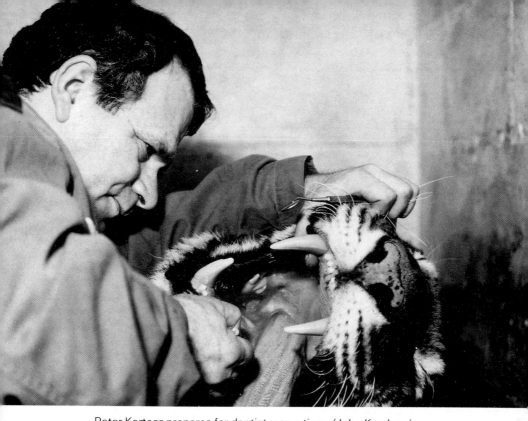

Peter Kertesz prepares for dentistry on a tiger. *(John Kershaw)*

Operating on a jaguar at Madrid Zoo, 1982. *(J M Martos)*

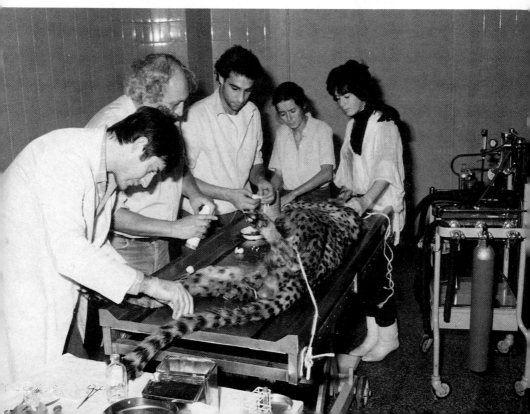

Figure 9 : Carte générale des côtes sahariennes atlantiques. Les principaux caps sont notés.

The coastline of Cap Blanc. *(Pierre Escoubet)*

The monk seal cliffs. *(Pierre Escoubet)*

Leaving the *El Hamiss* in search of monk seals. *(David Taylor)*

Lions at Luanda Zoo, Angola. *(David Taylor)*

Injecting a rutting camel that is foaming at the mouth can be tricky. *(Roger Dixon)*

One of the circus chimps in Greece. *(David Taylor)*

Llamas are hardy creatures, but still need medical check-ups. *(Roger Dixon)*

Back at our room in the officers' mess we took a look at the aphrodisiac powder. It resembled wood ash and smelled like Vick.

'Well,' said John, 'even if it doesn't work for X, he'll find it a different sort of birthday present, won't he?'

Two days later the *El Hamiss* came into harbour at last and once again we took onboard my party, the navy divers, the marines and all our gear. The military contingent had swelled in size and there seemed to be more weaponry, in addition to the extra Zodiacs we had requested. This time there was a severe shortage of bunk space and the captain warned us that fresh water would have to be carefully rationed if we were to lie off Cap Blanc for more than a few days. Showers were out. The fresh water supply would only be turned on for an hour each day.

It was my good fortune to have bagged the cabin of a second officer who was away on leave. John and I thus would have the use of our own bathroom – a matter of some importance as the new military doctor assigned to this second expedition went the way of his predecessor on the first when we were but two hours into the voyage. Like his colleague he came to me only when he was apple green in the face, took my Stugeron tablets too late and then retched, literally *ad nauseam*, throughout the vessel. He too retired to his bunk never to be seen again.

If anything the weather was even better when we arrived again off Cap Blanc. The sun blazed in a cloudless sky and the sea was glass smooth, but again with a long slow silent roll that produced a surface resembling a giant version of the distorting mirrors in Blackpool beach's Fun House. Once more as the engines were stopped with the ship's stern towards the coast, the marines set up their machine-gun position on the afterdeck and we scanned the cliffline through binoculars. Approaching the cliffs in Zodiacs we met occasional monk seals scouting for fish about a mile out at sea, but closer in a zone of suddenly rising rough waves kept us from inspecting the cave entrances and we were deafened by the steady thunder of the breakers. It was immensely disappointing but there was absolutely nothing to be done but wait again.

On one of our trips inshore on that first day I glimpsed what I momentarily thought were two tall and unusually shaped waves rising by the side of our dinghy. The gleaming black triangles, streaming with water, dipped and vanished and then rose again even higher to reveal the billiard-ball smooth backs of two mighty bodies – with the characteristic white curlicue designs we call 'saddle marks'. 'Killer whales! And there's another!' shouted John above the water's roar, pointing an arm to the opposite side of our lurching boat. The third whale's dorsal fin was curved, not quite sickle shaped – a female. As we turned slowly away from land we watched the trio of whales, two males and a female, swim steadily parallel to the cliffs and about one hundred yards away from them. They passed the entrances to 'our' monk seal caves and then turned round a hundred and eighty degrees and retraced their course. Again they turned and their dorsal fins cut through the water majestically as they rose to breathe every thirty seconds or so. Back and forth the three whales swam over a distance of about half a mile. I knew what they were up to. 'They're patrolling the seal grottos,' I shouted to John. 'Waiting to grab any seals leaving or entering.'

My companion nodded, his hair running with sea water. 'So on top of everything else the killers are another threat to the monk seals' survival!' he bellowed in reply.

As far as I knew killer whale activity of this kind had never before been reported from Cap Blanc. You can't blame the whales – they're very fond of seals and sealions if they can catch them, sometimes almost coming aground on beaches in Patagonia to seize South American sealion pups, and breaking through ice in Arctic waters as they hunt harp seals that have hauled out. Killer whales are very intelligent, powerful animals with a top speed exceeding that of any

other marine mammal, and an agility almost as great as that
of seals and dolphins. Armed with around fifty awesome,
conical teeth, they can weigh up to ten tons and will eat
anything from salmon to herring to walrus to chunks bitten
off the much bigger blue or fin whales. But killer whales are
to be found in all oceans and are not, at present, an
endangered species like the monk seal. Over the ages any
monk seals taken by killer whales would have been
balanced by the reproductive capacity of the flourishing
populations along the Mediterranean and Atlantic coasts.
Now, any losses to hungry whales could hasten the seals'
demise. As killer whales are also known to hunt and kill
just for fun, our discovery of the killer whale patrols
strengthened yet again my conviction that an attempt to set
up captive breeding groups for future reintroduction into
the wild was wholly justifiable.

There was nothing for it but to while away our time as
best we could and wait for the breakers to relent. Making
our fresh water supply last as long as possible became vital.
One evening the captain demonstrated how we could
shower satisfactorily with the parsimonious application of a
jam jar full of water, and ordered that henceforth the taps
should be turned on for only thirty minutes in twenty-four
hours. John, to my abiding astonishment, began cleaning
his teeth using water obtained from a flushing toilet.

The Lisa Stansfield videos and French or Egyptian B
films, censored by one of the officers, a devout Muslim, for
any display of *décolletage* or other lubricity that might
upset the company, ran from six a.m. until late at night.
The boiled sheep's heads at mealtimes were occasionally
replaced by fish – mullet or gilt-head – purchased over the
side from tiny, frail-looking Canarian boats crewed often by
only a couple of men. Both dishes were rescued from the
cook's remarkable ability to render all things unutterably
tasteless, by my foresight in bringing along for the second
voyage several bottles of Tabasco sauce and tins of jalapeno
peppers. We spent hours on the bridge watching the radar

tracking the swarms of illegally fishing trawlers and staring
through binoculars at the coastline. The breakers continued
to pound the shore. John lay on his bunk reading Thomas
Hardy. Roger was deep into the Koran. I did my rounds,
checking on the health of the still bilious doctor, discussing
and planning with Mohammed, Said and Pierre for when
and if we made our assault on the caves, surreptitiously
sipping whisky with one of the Moroccan officers in his
cabin and, most of all, writing.

As the days passed, both John and I became increasingly
depressed. What many folk would have thought a 'glamorous'
expedition, was becoming deeply boring. Better by far, I
thought, to be back at Chessington doing the weekly rounds
of the tapirs and ocelots and giraffes with Chris the head
keeper, or out at Golders Hill Park performing some minor
operation on a wallaby or deer, or inspecting the animals at
Gerry Cottle's Circus. I missed being in touch with events
by phone or fax. *El Hamiss* could talk by telex, but only
unreliably and on service matters, with the naval base at
Agadir. What if the pandas in Madrid or the whales in
Antibes or the dolphins in Riccione were in trouble? My
partners John and Andrew, would handle any emergencies
impeccably, sure enough, but I would have dearly liked to
have known what was going on, and if any of *my* animals –
patients, friends, that I'd known and worked with in some
cases for twenty years or more – were in trouble. Harvey,
the dolphin at Costa Brava, Hattie the hippo at Windsor,
Copito de Nieve, the albino gorilla at Barcelona, Freya, the
pregnant French killer whale, and so many, many more.
Were they OK? I'd travelled to over thirty countries in the
course of my career as peripatetic exotic animal veterinarian
and always, somehow, from Greenland to Panama, China
to Czechoslovakia, managed to keep in regular touch with
my base. When Chang-Chang the giant panda baby
produced by artificial insemination at Madrid Zoo had at
last been born, I'd been down in the deserts of Arabia, but
I'd heard of the great event within a couple of hours of his

arrival. Since setting up the IZVG in 1969 I had been on duty, on call, twenty-four hours a day, 365 days a year. On call – that was the point. Without any facility to communicate, I felt marooned, halfway down the coast of Africa.

Eventually, with the fresh-water tanks of *El Hamiss* getting towards three-quarters empty, I was faced with the likelihood of having to call off the expedition again, and this time for at least another year. Then, one morning, we awoke to find our vessel enveloped in fog. The thick white vapour clung tightly to a sea that seemed even stiller than before, and suffocated the familiar sounds of the birds and the breezes among the superstructure. 'Could be our lucky day,' said John as we stood looking towards the invisible land. 'Fancy a run in?'

I did, and a few minutes later we were sitting in the biggest of the Zodiacs with a second officer at the controls of the inboard motor as the ship disgorged us through the watertight doors at the stern. With a compass bearing set on the seal caves and the engine throbs echoing in the cocooning fog, we nosed slowly away from the *El Hamiss*. Within seconds the corvette could no longer be seen and we seemed to be sailing through clouds, air- rather than waterborne. The Moroccan naval officer stood amidships at his wheel with me behind him clinging on to a rail and John at the front facing towards us with his bottom on the rubber wall of the Zodiac. As we cautiously edged towards the cliffs, the long rollers made themselves felt once again, and our progress resembled a ride on the Big Dipper. The fog continued to enfold us in its clammy embrace. I was straining to see into the whiteness ahead of us from where I imagined I could hear the first sounds of crashing water. The officer was intent on his compass and controls, moving us very slowly now for fear of running on to the unseen rocks. John was concentrating on holding on, as spray veiled his shoulders. No one spoke.

All at once the expression on my friend's face changed to one of sheer horror. Eyes bulging, mouth wide open, he managed to yell two words in French: 'Shit! Look!' He was staring at something behind us. The officer and I turned our heads simultaneously. Towering over us so high that it disappeared into the fog above the Zodiac was a solid, bottle-green wall of water. It must have been over twenty feet high. The sea had reared silently into a giant breaker that was going, within seconds, to explode over us. Thousands of tons of water were poised to destroy us as its mist-shrouded crest broke in a furious drum roll of sound. As if by reflex the Moroccan skipper spun his wheel and brought the bows of the Zodiac swinging round so that they jutted into the dark face of the great wave. Our engine screamed frantically as he thrust open the throttle and we began, to my horrified amazement, to climb almost vertically up the wall of water. Up and up we went and for an instant seemed to perch on the razor edge of the crest. It was beginning to break when we tipped violently forward over its back and shot down the sheer drop on the other side. Through the din I heard John yell. We were tossed about like a rubber ball on landing in the deep trough behind the wave. White foam laced the fog-laden air as the broken wave behind us thrashed in its death throes. I caught a glimpse of black rocks – the cliffs were only yards away. It was a miracle that John hadn't been thrown out of the Zodiac. I was hanging on like grim death while the officer, pale-faced and tense, wrestled with the bucking wheel and constantly brushed away water that was flooding over the glass of the compass.

'*Encore!*' shouted John who had now turned to look forward, and there before us rising up through the fog was another dark-green wall of water. Again a quick display of fine seamanship on the part of our skipper as we climbed over its summit and plummeted into the next trough, just in the nick of time. But it hadn't been quite as high as the first and when we rolled over the third and the fourth, each less menacing than the one before, my pulse dropped to a more reasonable rate and I began to produce saliva again. We reached smooth ocean at last, and after some minutes to my great relief could make out the ghostly shape of the *El Hamiss* emerging from the mist. The ship's doors opened and we charged up the metal slipway into safety. All three of us climbed out of the Zodiac in stunned silence. John and I said nothing until we had mugs of hot coffee in our hands. The officer who had skippered the Zodiac came and sat with us. He was still unusually pale. Eventually he spoke, slowly and very quietly. 'We were very nearly goners,' he said. 'If that first wave had broken . . .'

Some of the others came to hear what had happened. 'Like my guys say,' said the leader of the navy divers. 'It would be a deathwish to enter those caves, they want no part of it.'

A little while later the captain called me up to his cabin and showed me a telex from Agadir naval base. Storms were on their way down the coast. The *El Hamiss* would have to steam back at once to the protected waters of Dakhla. I called my team together as we raised anchor and told them of my decision to call off the monk seal venture for 1990. Roger was keen to return for a third time after the *El Hamiss* had taken on water, fuel and other stores, and Mohammed was also prepared to try again without delay. But the usual autumn 'window' of good weather at Cap Blanc was at an end. The monk seal experiment would have to wait for another year at least.

John and I returned to Antibes, empty handed – except for the present of aphrodisiac powder for X. He tried it out as instructed. It didn't work either.

5
The Junkie Chimp

It is to what I have called the Apes of God that I am drawing
your attention . . .

P Wyndham Lewis, *The Apes of God*

Viva España! Wow! This was what it was all about: sea,
sun, sangria and sex. Lots and lots of each. The Lambada
blasted out from the loudspeaker over the beach-bar where
a queue of boiled-lobster-coloured Brits were lined up for
San Migs and Bacardi and Cokes. All the pedalos were out
at sea and, as usual, the Germans had annexed every one of
the lilos round the swimming pool. Must have been down
with their towels as soon as they came back pissed in the
wee small hours.

There was, as ever when the sun was at its height, the
smell of hot fat – an exotic blend of olive oil, Ambre Solaire
and human sebum. As the Thompsons rep had promised at
the first night champagne – oops! sorry, we're not allowed
to use that C word since the French kicked up a fuss – at
the first night *cava* reception, everyone was having one hell
of a holiday.

If he'd been able to speak the little chimpanzee sitting in a
cardboard box in the room at the back of the beach-bar
might have begged to differ. He was having one hell of a
time – literally. Time had flown by at a bewildering speed.
Three weeks ago, when most of the holidaymakers out
there had been still at home in Birmingham, Copenhagen or
Düsseldorf, he'd been even further away than them, happily
roaming through a stand of wild bananas with his family.
What happened then was a blurred, horrific nightmare.

Noise, deafening noise. Strange, fearful smells. His father lying unusually still and silent. His mother moaning softly, her breasts shining red. Panicking, he had felt himself seized, arm-wrenched into a full nelson. Then there was darkness, solitude, and more strange, terrifying smells and sounds. He'd suddenly awakened from the long nightmare, if that is what it was, to find himself in the cardboard box. With a banana. At least he wasn't on his own. He looked across the room at the big male chimpanzee sitting on the table. Bigger than his father and with a pink freckled face unlike his father's black one, the older chimp was indifferent towards him. It seemed that all he was concerned with was the man who sat at the table. The big chimp watched him with fixed and staring eyes.

The man, a handsome Spaniard with the dark complexion of one whose roots were in Andalucia and its Moorish past, was preparing to roll a cigarette. He hummed a *gitano* melody softly as he sprinkled a generous pinch of Moroccan Gold on to the tobacco, licked one edge of the paper and deftly rolled the joint. '*Vale*, Paco,' he murmured. '*Vale*. First though, your pill.' He put his hand in a pocket and withdrew a small blue tablet. '*Abre la boca*, Paco, open your gob.' Paco just stared at him vacantly. The man smacked him once hard across a cheek, rocking him so that he almost fell off the table. '*Abre la boca*,' repeated the man without raising his voice, and the big chimp opened his mouth. The man popped in the tablet and Paco began to chew. 'Good boy, Paco,' said the man. 'Now you can have your present.'

He handed the joint to the chimpanzee who took it with finger and thumb and placed it between his lips. The man flicked a lighter and put the flame to the twisted end of the dope-laden cigarette. Paco inhaled deeply, held his breath and then exhaled blue smoke down his nostrils. He continued to stare at the man. The Spaniard rose from his chair, picked up the camera bag and slipped half a dozen rolls of spare film into the back pocket of his jeans. Paco took another drag on his joint. His eyes glazed ever so slightly. '*Dios te salve Maria*,' hummed the man. 'OK, Paco, time to go to work.' He took an old leather dog collar from a shelf, slipped it around the chimpanzee's neck, fastened it and clipped on a length of chain lead. Paco knew what to do. The man crooked his arm and Paco climbed on to it, leaning on the man's shoulder so that it took most of his weight. '*Dios te salve Maria*,' sang the man as he went out of the door, locking it behind him. 'Maria *olé, olé, olé.*'

High from the marijuana and Valium cocktail, Paco was beginning to feel, just like the tourists among whom they made their way, that it was in truth a most wonderful day.

Fate, the fate which ordained that Paco and I should eventually meet, came in the shape of a hippopotamus, not that there were any hippos cavorting in the shallows on the beach at Javea where Paco and his master had their beat. No, the fateful hippopotamus was one in the Safari Park at Vergel, a few miles inland, and it had me flying down to the Costa Blanca one summer's day when it bit off, clean as a whistle, half the trunk of an elephant. The greatly shortened proboscis healed well after treatment and its owner quickly learned how to pick up apples by kicking them into a pile with its feet and then kneeling down to employ what was left of its trunk in the usual way, even though the delicate 'fingers' on the tip were no longer there. I was at the Safari Park having coffee with the director at the end of a visit to check on the elephant's progress when the telephonist buzzed him. There was a man at the gate wanting some help with a chimpanzee. 'Come with me, doctor,' said the director. 'It sounds more like something in your line.'

Standing beside the pay booth was a young man with long black hair, long black fingernails and a fat gold earring. He was wearing grubby jeans, a purple Hendrix T-shirt and Raybans. At his feet squatted a fully grown male chimp on a collar and lead. The chimp's face bore a vacant expression. I recognized the look at once – it was doped, just like some poor motorcycling chimpanzees I'd seen years before at a circus in Panama. '*Buenas tardes,*' said the man, flashing a gold incisor crown. 'I am Pepe. Pepe Almohada.'

'*Buenas tardes,*' replied the director. 'This is our veterinary consultant, Doctor Taylor. You have some difficulties?'

The man smiled with his mouth, took off his Raybans and his dark eyes between half-closed lids regarded me with open suspicion. '*Sí* – well, nothing much really. Paco, my pet here, seems to have a little toothache. I gave him aspirin and Novalgina, but I think it's still troubling him.'

'How does it affect him?' I asked. 'Difficulty in eating? Tenderness if you touch his mouth?' I squatted on my haunches in front of the chimpanzee who stared glassily straight through me.

'He bit a friend of mine,' said Almohada. 'Normally he's so good, so sweet. My baby! My pet!' He took out a comb and ran it through his hair. Arrogant lying bastard, I thought.

Cautiously I put out a hand and stroked Paco on his head. He seemed unaware of my touch. I slid a finger down the side of his right cheek and in between his lips. Tensing, ready for the first sign of him biting, I flapped down the lower lip and then worked my finger round to the front of his mouth. That gave me a good view of his teeth. The cause of the trouble was plain to see. Paco certainly must have had toothache – throbbing, agonizing toothache, for at the base of the lower left canine or fang tooth, the gum was swollen, angry red and perforated by a small hole from which watery pus was leaking. 'A great big tooth root abscess,' I pronounced, but it wasn't the abscess that held my attention. Rather it was the four fang teeth; each one had been broken off more or less level with the gum, and it was down the exposed central pulp cavity of one of these teeth that infection had entered and set up the mother of all gumboils. No time to mince words. '*Señor,*' I said rising to my feet, 'I assume you are a beach photographer?'

Almohada wasn't smiling now. 'So. Yes. I am a photographer, but what has that got to do with my pet, Paco?'

'I've seen chimps like Paco before,' I said. 'Four teeth broken off. How did you do it? Pliers? Hammer? Filled him up with a handful of sleeping pills first?'

The photographer looked at me with undisguised hatred. 'Hey!' he said to the director. 'What's this Anglo on about? Is he some *idiota* or what? I meet people like him sometimes in Javea. *Yayas Inglesas dementes.* Crazy English grannies. *Con gatos*,' he added for good measure. 'With cats.' I think he was referring to those indomitable English expats who spread the gospel of animal welfare among the natives when they retire overseas – the ladies who care for the cats of Venice or support the Brooke Hospital for Horses in Cairo. God bless 'em all.

'OK, so I'm a *yaya*,' I said. 'But you know bloody well what happened. When Paco became sexually mature and naturally aggressive living his rotten, frustrated, artificial life, you did what many of your kind do – trimmed off his most dangerous biting teeth. For the sake of your business. Can't have Paco taking chunks out of English lager louts on the beach, even if they are stupid enough to want a souvenir photograph to take back home.'

'*Oye!*' shouted Almohada. He tapped the director on the chest. 'I came to see you, *señor*, not this stranger. All I want is some medicine for the animal. I'll pay for it.'

'But I am not a *veterinario*,' said the director indignantly. 'And please don't prod me in the chest, *señor*.'

Almohada spat in the dust and cursed vehemently in a dialect I could not understand.

'Look,' I said. 'The important thing is that this chimpanzee is suffering. I'll treat him here and now – it will mean taking the tooth out.'

'How you take the tooth out?' Almohada hissed the question.

'Anaesthetic, forceps.'

'If you kill him, I kill you.'

I ignored the threat. 'Bring him over to the office,' I said. 'And keep your trap shut.'

The atmosphere in the office that boiling hot afternoon was icy to say the least as I prepared to extract Paco's tooth. The director looked glum, Almohada kept rolling his eyes and muttering imprecations under his breath, and I tried to concentrate on the work in hand. As I looked in more detail at the chimpanzee I became more convinced than ever that the animal was under the influence of drugs of some kind, probably hashish or tranquillizers. Suppose they interacted with the anaesthetic? '*Señor* Almohada,' I said as I inspected Paco's enormous pupils. 'You'd perhaps kill Paco if you don't tell me the truth. Has he had any drugs?'

'Drugs?' The photographer looked at me, his face twisted with anger. 'What you think – I use drugs? Paco uses drugs? Are you *loco*?'

'Just asking,' I replied. 'Drugs and anaesthetics don't go together.' He said nothing and I filled the syringe with ketamine. The chimp sat glassy-eyed on a chair while I injected his arm. Five minutes later Paco was unconscious and I checked his respiration, pulse and capillary refill time. It was then, as I pressed a finger on them to see how quickly the blanched area was recharged with blood, that I noticed a faint yellow tinge of the gums. Parting the hair on his chest I imagined I could see it in the pale skin colour also.

'Is he OK?' whispered Almohada lighting a cigarette with trembling hands. His venom seemed to have drained away leaving more agitation than anger.

'Has he had drugs, *señor*?' I asked again.

He hesitated, pulled on his cigarette and then said quietly, 'Hash.'

'How much?'

'Two joints. He loves the smoke, doctor, you know, a little fun.' He managed a wink. Then, agitated again, he said, 'Is he going to be OK, doctor? Him and me we're partners.'

It didn't take more than a couple of minutes to extract the remainder of the tooth which was mainly root. With a steel probe and then a syringe full of warm saline I cleaned out the abscess. Paco was beginning to stir as I gave him a final shot of penicillin. As he lay on the table moving his tongue slowly, I noticed again the pale yellow tinge within his mouth. Before he came round completely I took a vacutainer from my bag and drew off ten millilitres of blood from his arm for later analysis.

'How much do I pay?' said Almohada as he carried Paco out to his car.

'Nothing – this time,' I replied. I was certain I hadn't finished with the chimpanzee.

'*Madre de Dios*!' said the director, breathing a sigh of relief as they drove away. 'That was a pair. A *cabrón* of a low-life photographer and a junky chimpanzee.' He shook his head. 'I need a drink. Let me buy you a cold beer, doctor.'

Later that day I flew back to London. As soon as I landed I contacted the Ministry of Agriculture to arrange a special licence for importation of the chimpanzee blood I was carrying. Whilst I have a blanket permit to import material from marine mammals, with the exception of grey whales and certain seals, species in which a virus similar to that which causes an important disease of domestic pigs has been found occasionally, the ministry must license every import of blood serum or unpreserved bits of tissue from primates and other animals such as cattle, antelopes, etc. In the primate material there could be deadly disease organisms like the ones causing Lassa fever or Marburg disease in man and the samples from hoofed stock might inadvertently introduce foot-and-mouth-disease or rinderpest into the country's farm stock. Paco worried me. It wasn't just that yellow tinge to his gums and skin. The whole idea of beach photographers using chimpanzees and other animals – in the Canary Islands I'd even seen a snow leopard cub being used – is repugnant to me. The animals are acquired from some highly dubious source, generally being smuggled in. They are kept in very poor conditions, the photographers know little or nothing about their nutrition and other needs, and when species such as chimpanzees, monkeys and wild cats become more and troublesome, they are heavily doped, killed or abandoned. And it still goes on. Tourists who are willing to pay several pounds to have a Polaroid snap taken of themselves with an exotic animal – oh, what a laugh when we show it to the regulars at the pub or Bierkeller – still exist. Some beach photographers rake in small fortunes during the high season. Paco, ten years old I estimated, was already approaching the end of his usefulness.

I was packing the vial of chimp's blood into a padded packet for sending to the public health laboratory for hepatitis screening, when I suddenly had an idea. I drew off half the serum with a syringe and put it into another vial. The public health virologists would have more than enough with their sample. The other half I would send express to another laboratory with a letter explaining what I required.

One week passed and at last the laboratory results arrived. I lost no time in booking a seat on the next flight to Valencia. Although this was to be the final checkup on the elephant's trunk, my main purpose concerned Paco. The elephant was doing splendidly and learning each day to cope better with her abbreviated member. It was even proving to be somewhat of an advantage – members of the public, fascinated by her curious appearance, threw her more than her fair share of buns and apples. I explained to the director that the sample of blood from Paco had proved positive for hepatitis A. 'We must find Almohada and his chimp,' I said. 'The animal is ill and the man is at risk. His chimp can easily infect him.'

'But we don't have an address for him, doctor.'

'He said he worked the beach at Javea. Drive me down

there, and if you don't mind, stop at the offices of the Guardia Civil on the way. We need one of the boys in green.'

The director, a kindly man who owned the largest orange-tree plantation in the province, raised his eyebrows. 'The Guardia? What on earth for?'

'To get Paco. Take him away from the bastard who's exploiting him.'

'But the Guardia. You know them. They won't lift a finger for a photographer's monkey. Anyway he *belongs* to the guy. If you try to snatch Paco, the Guardia will come looking for *you*, doctor.'

'That's not the way it's going to be, I promise you. Come on, let's go to Javea.'

The chief sat behind his desk wearing the polished black *tricornio* hat, rarely seen nowadays except on ceremonial occasions. He was a plumper version of Peter Sellers playing Clouseau. A Ducados dangled from his lips, trails of ash lying undisturbed on the generous outcurve of his green-uniformed jacket. The director and I sat on chairs, lower than his, in front of the desk.

'And what do you expect the Guardia Civil to do for you, *señores*?' His voice, long matured on black tobacco and cognac, rumbled like a sherry cask being rolled along a cobbled street. 'Crime, thuggery, violence and murder are our business. We are not those *peóns*, the *Policía Municipal*.' Full of self-importance, he tapped the pistol in the black holster at his side. 'A monkey is a monkey, no? The Guardia aren't monkey catchers.'

'But times have changed, *señor*,' I said. 'Now Spain, along with the rest of the European Community, is taking practical measures to enforce the Washington Convention.'

'*Qué?*'

'The Washington Convention that protects animals in danger from illegal importation and exportation.'

'Aah.' The chief looked at his watch.

Long after they'd signed the so-called CITES Convention,

many countries chose either to ignore or merely paid lip service to the control of the shadowy trade in species included within its schedules. In Europe, Spain and Belgium had been the main offenders and, as I write, blatant contraventions of the regulations still take place regularly in the Iberian Peninsula. But things were showing signs of changing and the CITES office in Madrid now had a concerned and dynamic woman in charge who was beginning to make headway against the indolence and in-efficiency of bureaucrats, particularly those in His Majesty's Customs.

'You know, *señor jefe*,' I continued. 'The Guardia Civil has recently been given the responsibility for dealing with the illegal importers of animals. Some of the latter are unscrupulous villains who can cut up rough. Who but the Guardia could take them on? Indeed the Guardia is soon to form a special task force purely to work on such cases.'

The Guardia chief stubbed out his cigarette with a flourish of a podgy hand that made the diamond ring on his little finger flash brilliantly. 'I have not heard of that,' he said. 'But I can see the wisdom of such a strategy. I shot a gorilla once in Rio Muni.'

Ignoring the distasteful *non sequitur* I said, 'There is a beach photographer in Javea – a man called Almohada – who almost certainly has no licence for his chimpanzee. Do you know him?'

He smiled and puffed out his chest, dislodging the cigarette ash which tumbled down his belly in a minute grey avalanche.

'*Señor. Nothing*, but nothing, in Javea escapes my notice. I know every gypsy pickpocket, every thief working the villas of the English and Dutch residents, every foreigner without a work permit. Almohada I know too. A *gitano* who chases the girls. Well, he causes no trouble. Takes photographs of the *turistas* with his monkey every summer. I'm not sure I can ...'

'*Señor jefe*, this is very important. Illegal importation of an endangered animal. You are entitled to demand to see his licence.'

'But I am a man of action, not paperwork.' He fingered his pistol again.

'Would it be best for me to contact Madrid direct? Maybe the Guardia . . .'

The chief looked at me sharply. '*Señor*, let's get this very clear. *I* am the Guardia Civil in this region. No need to involve *Madrid*.' He uttered the name of the capital with a sour twist of his lips. Many citizens of Alicante province, like their compatriots in Cataluña, have little time for the Castilians. 'But you can leave everything to me. I will inspect his licence when I have time. There is so much work.'

I knew what that meant. Nothing would happen. But all was not lost, for I had two more cards to play and one was an ace. I reached into my bag, pulled out two documents and placed them on the desk in front of the chief. 'There are additional problems with Almohada,' I said slowly. 'I took a blood sample last week from his chimpanzee. This laboratory report shows that it is infected with the hepatitis A virus – very infectious to humans. Almohada and all his customers are at serious risk in handling, even being near the animal. Just imagine if there is an epidemic among the *turistas*. The mayor, the townspeople – they would be *devastated*. Think of the implications, the publicity.'

With his eyes narrowed the chief looked even more like Clouseau. 'And then there is this!' I indicated the other piece of paper. It too was a laboratory report from the institute near Newmarket which is a world leader in screening blood and urine from horses for evidence of doping. With their techniques the scientists at the laboratory could identify the minutest amounts of unusual substances in body fluids or bits of blood. I'd occasionally used them in the past in suspected cases of poisoning, most notably where some cheetahs at Windsor Safari Park had been affected by barbiturates used to euthanase a cow, the meat from which was subsequently sold to the park for feeding to the big cats.

'If I may translate for you, *señor jefe*,' I said standing up, the better to point out the relevant words. 'It says "serum sample from chimpanzee adult male. Reference Almohada, Javea." And then, here, "traces of the following substances were found." And below are the important words. "Diazepam", that's Valium, "Cannabinol", that's a constituent of marijuana, "Cocaine", you know what that is. Señor Almohada is giving his chimp illegal narcotics. Maybe he himself is a *drogadicto*.'

The head of the Javea Guardia rocked heavily back in his chair and hurriedly lit another cigarette before speaking. '*Increíble! Increíble!*' he murmured and then he reached under his desk to press a hidden button. A buzzer sounded in the outer office and presently an aide came scuttling in. Returning the man's salute, the chief barked, 'Gorena! Bring the car! Get Chirico and Piza as well. We go at once to the *playa*!'

It must have been a really special treat for the tourists queuing for their drinks and ice-cream when our little band arrived at the bar on the beach. There was *el jefe* himself, his three Guardia Civil henchmen, the director and me. The chief marched, full of self-importance, to the head of the queue. 'Is Almohada around?' he snapped at the bartender. The latter turned to his shelf of bottles, selected an old Carlos Primero and poured a generous measure into a balloon glass which he pushed towards the Guardia chief before answering. '*Sí, jefe*, he's in his room back there. Had the flu for a couple of days. Not been working.'

The chief glanced surreptitiously in our direction before downing the cognac in one. He grunted a barely audible '*Gracias*' to the bartender and then said loudly so that all the waiting tourists could hear '*Vamonos!* Round the back, men!'

We all walked round to the rear of the low building, our

numbers trebled by the tourists, including several small and excited English children, who decided to come along. *El jefe* banged a meaty fist on a faded red door.

'What's going on?' shouted a breathless English boy who had just arrived at the double.

'The fat chap in the daft hat has got a murderer cornered in there,' answered another.

'Kick the door in, Die Hard!' yelled a third.

The chief, who didn't speak a word of English, looked back benevolently at his small flock of young supporters and patted one on the head. Then he thumped on the door again. 'Almohada – are you in there?' he shouted.

The sound of a reedy voice came from within. '*Sí*. Come in.'

Pulling his pistol from its holster to the 'oohs' and 'aahs' of the tourists, *el jefe* lifted the latch and pushed the door open. Over the shoulders of the four Guardia packed into the doorway I glimpsed the interior of the shabby room. A chimpanzee, Paco, sat motionless in a small cage of thick iron bars set against the far wall. Another, much younger chimp, peeped over the edge of a cardboard box nearby, chattering its teeth silently, a startled expression fixed on its small pale face. In the centre of the room was a table littered with empty bottles, food scraps and cigarette stubs. Apart from a large coloured poster of Kim Bassinger on one wall and a crucifix on the other, the only other object in the room was a low bed. Lying on it, naked from the waist up was Almohada. He was sweating profusely – large drops of perspiration beading his face and chest. His skin colour was that of a freshly opened primrose in spring. The photographer, it was plain to see, even at a distance of some twenty feet, had hepatitis.

Events from then on moved swiftly. An ambulance was called for, Almohada was stretchered away, the Guardia began a search of his room, and the director and I dealt with the chimpanzees. I injected both of them with gamma-globulin that I'd brought out from England and Paco,

whose yellow tinge was now distinct, also got a drink of
fruit juice heavily laced with arginine oxo-glucurate to
support his liver. He took his medicine without complain-
ing. 'I, in the name of the Guardia Civil, order the
confiscation of these animals until all licences appertaining
to them have been produced,' announced the chief a little
while later to no one in particular. His men had discovered
a cache of Valium tablets, cocaine powder, cannabis 'grass'
and assorted barbiturate sleeping pills in a guitar lying
under the bed. As one of them shook the drugs out through
the instrument's sound-hole, the chief tugged at a crease in
his jacket and adjusted his *tricornio*, tipping its brim lower
over his eyes and giving him a more bellicose appearance.
'We have a serious crime here,' he rumbled. 'Drugs and the
scum who peddle them. God knows what this country
would be like without the Guardia now that El Caudillo is
no more.' He hushed his voice reverently as he uttered the
title of his beloved Franco.

'If you are confiscating the chimpanzees,' I said, 'a most
wise and correct decision, if I may say so, *señor jefe*, where
do you plan to house them?'

The chief's self-satisfied expression vanished. 'Err . . .
well . . . err . . . The jail is not . . . err . . . what do you
suggest, *señor director*?'

The Safari Park director sighed loudly. 'If, as Doctor
Taylor says, at least one of these animals is infected with
hepatitis, I cannot take them – too much risk to my stock.
But there is an empty tack room with grilled windows in the
stables of my *finca*. They could go there temporarily.'

'And I will make arrangements for them then to be
transferred to the chimp sanctuary near Barcelona,' I said.
An English couple had established the sanctuary several
years before, and were doing Trojan work in rehabilitating
some of the tiny percentage of illegally imported primates
confiscated by Customs at Spanish airports.

'*Excelente!*' said the chief. 'I will inform headquarters in
Madrid of my successful operation without delay. The

papers authorizing the detention of the monkeys will be signed by tomorrow.'

Paco and the little chimp – we didn't know his name, so I christened him Paquito, little Paco – had been sitting quietly watching the proceedings throughout, and each held one of my hands as I walked them out of the room. Passing the table Paco spotted a single unlit Ducados lying on top of it. With a lightning movement of his free hand he snatched up the cigarette and put it between his lips. He looked up at me – without doubt wanting a light. I took the cigarette from him gently and threw it over my shoulder. He didn't react in the slightest at being robbed of his fag. 'You are giving up smoking, my son,' I said. 'I just wouldn't know what to do for a chimpanzee with a smoker's cough.' In the director's car I sat in the back with a chimp on each knee. Paco sneakily, and to no avail, used one finger to root in the ashtray looking for dog ends.

Three weeks later the two chimpanzees were on their way up to Barcelona. Paco's abscess had healed and as his mild attack of hepatitis cleared, the jaundice faded. I had arranged for Peter Kertesz, the Mayfair dental surgeon who works with us on the more complicated cases of mouth disease in wild animals, to fly over and do root treatments and fillings on his broken teeth. The characters of both animals had changed dramatically in the short space of time since their rescue from the beach. Paquito became the inquisitive, ever active and mischievous individual that a baby chimp should be and his relationship with Paco was that of a hero-worshipping younger brother. Paco, his system clean of drugs and eating lots of fresh vegetables, fruit and a little cooked chicken or hard-boiled egg each day, was no longer a stupefied zombie, and spent all and every day climbing, leaping and somersaulting in the large tree-filled enclosure they shared with two old female chimpanzees, who had welcomed them quite literally with open arms and joyful screeches. Almohada also recovered from his hepatitis, but in the hospital of a prison near Alicante at the beginning of a two-year sentence.

It was with a profound feeling of, for once, having achieved something practical in the struggle against beach photographers and their ilk, that I went to see Paco and Paquito later that year when I was in Barcelona to do the annual insurance medical on Ulysses, the killer whale at the city zoo. The two chimpanzees were in the pink, their coats now fuller and displaying a healthy sheen, and they had clearly formed a firm social bond with the two females. Best of all I was recognized, at least by Paco. Chimpanzees don't forget people who stick needles into them and I was delighted to stand in front of his enclosure while Paco, a glassy-eyed junkie no longer, shrieked insults at me. But Paco and Paquito are just a lucky two out of the unknown total, almost certainly hundreds, of chimpanzees and other exotic animals that continue to be maltreated round the coasts of Spain alone.

By 1990 it was very gratifying to find the Guardia Civil's newly formed task force for CITES enforcement beginning to show it had teeth – and was prepared to bite. A thoroughly planned raid was carried out by the Guardia and an animal protection organization on the beach photographers of Gran Canaria. Only one photographer could produce anything like a valid import licence for his chimpanzee, many were tipped off, probably by informers in positions of authority in the municipalities or even in the Guardia, and quickly made themselves and their animals scarce, but after a lot of verbal and some physical battling, four chimpanzees were seized. My partner, John Lewis, had been asked to accompany raiding parties of Guardia on their 'swoops' in order to take immediate care of confiscated animals. Part of the operation was filmed for the 'Challenge Anneka' television programme which had organized the lightning construction of a superb primate unit to house rescued chimps at Monkey World in England. The four chimpanzees, all between one and two years of age, were flown to Heathrow airport where I met them in the middle of the night to check their condition. They were jet-lagged and very thirsty and took the plastic cups full of Coca-Cola that I handed them with perfect manners, drinking greedily. As well as being beverages that are well accepted by young primates, cola drinks also contain useful amounts of carbonic acid, potassium and sugar, very beneficial for weary little travellers. Once they had quenched their thirst, the young chimps set off on the last leg of their journey in a special quarantine van, and a couple of hours later were starting to settle down in their new home. Lots of photographers, of the *safe* sort, were there to welcome them and there wasn't a beach or a single tourist in sight, just dawn breaking over the peaceful Dorset countryside. The chimpanzee rescue operations by the Guardia Civil will continue.

6
Animal Showbiz

Authors and uncaptured criminals ... are the only people
free from routine.

Eric Linklater, *Poet's Pub*

'Don't move, sir, or the dogs'll have you!' said the
policeman, his thick-set body planted firmly against the
back of the exit door. He had slipped in while we were
concentrating on positioning the big cats. The two German
shepherds strained silently towards me on the leashes he
grasped in large red hands.

'I'm off for lunch,' I replied, nettled.

'You're not, sir – not till the dogs have been in there and
given it the once over, and the CID say you can.'

'Take your dogs in there and you'll cause bloody hell to
break loose, I promise you!'

'And why might that be, sir?' He tilted his head back and
looked down his nose with the world-weary expression of
one who had heard it all before.

'The leopards will go berserk. Your pair will be lucky to
last more than a minute.'

'Leopards, leo-pards? What are you on about, sir?' He
heavily over-emphasized the last word.

'Four black leopards. Loose. Eat your two puppies for
starters. So you *don't* go in until we know what this is all
about, and put the leopards back into their travelling crates.
But first I'm off to the pub across the road for my lunch.'

'You are going nowhere, sir.'

I was joined by the film crew, also bent on finding a pie
and a pint after a long morning's work.

'*No one* leaves,' the police dog handler announced sternly.

'Why not?' asked the film director, his face reddening rapidly.

'Can't say, sir.'

'You can't imprison us here without explanation or arrest,' I protested. At that point there was a knock on the door and the policeman moved to open it. A young man with shoulder-length greasy hair, designer stubble and jeans fashionably tattered open at the knees, entered the corridor. Behind him outside the doorway I could see an arc, shoulder to shoulder, of about a dozen uniformed policemen.

'These blokes want out, sir,' said the dog handler addressing the young man in a new and respectful tone of voice. 'And this chappie here is giving me some blarney about leo-pards,' he again pronounced the word as two, jabbing a fat red finger towards me.

'Makes a change from the pitbulls they've taken to using lately.' 'Tattered Jeans', apparently a plainclothes officer, looked us over. He seemed cross. 'All right constable,' he murmured. 'Leave this to me. Now – which of you fellows is the boss of this place? You?' He directed his question at me.

Another handful of young men, also in plainclothes appeared at that moment from somewhere in the building and closed in behind us. Surprising – I'd thought that apart from a caretaker, the film crew, the animal handler and I had been alone in the sparsely furnished warehouse.

'We want our lunch,' growled the film director.

'You can't leave the building till we've finished our dog search,' said 'Tattered Jeans' acerbically.

'If you take your dogs in there, you'll find four adult black leopards. They're fast, agile and fierce,' I said, enunciating each word clearly and slowly. 'And you will be held personally responsible if they go ape-shit and injure themselves or any of us. As for your German shepherds, they wouldn't know what hit them. Just one of those cats can take on a fully grown gorilla or a young lion and expect to win. So what is your name and number?' I thought for a moment from the expression on his face and the rhythmic way he clenched and unclenched his fists, that the plainclothes man was about to go for my throat.

'Before we go into all that,' he said, voice quiet and full of venom, 'what's this shit about leopards and who the hell are you lot?'

We very often supervise the welfare of exotic animals used in films and television commercials. Our function is to ensure that directors don't overwork the animals or ask them to do anything potentially harmful to themselves for the sake of art, and also, where dangerous species are involved, to stand by with dart weapons and drugs in case they should by any chance run amok. It is generally very boring work. The animals are provided by experts who know their fads and foibles intimately and can handle them with skill, humanity and, in the vast majority of cases, an abundance of love and respect. Some animal 'performers' are highly trained and have far more studio experience than the actors or models they work with. Bright lights, colourful scenery, the smell of makeup and the need to do repeated takes because human actors fluff their lines, never faze them. Individuals like the king penguin from Chessington Zoo, Pringle, positively revel in treading the boards, making a fuss only when it's time to go home. And as I've written elsewhere, Lock, the orang-utan friend and patient of mine who starred with Clint Eastwood in *Every Which Way But Loose* is a master at giving a perfect performance after being shown what to do only once, and provides the director with just what he wants in a single take. Not many human actors do that.

So most of the time I, or one of my partners, sit on a fold-up director's chair on the set and do nothing but watch, hour after hour. I find it useful for writing (as I am at this moment, dear reader, in a studio on the South Bank for an episode of TV's 'Drop the Dead Donkey') and there's always Haydn or Vivaldi on my Walkman. Although the tranquillizing equipment and first-aid drug kit are always close at hand, I have rarely had to use either. Only one animal in my care has ever died while 'working' at a studio, and that was a large black scorpion which I had been demonstrating on a children's television programme, 'Nature Trail', at Border Television in Carlisle. Why this happened I never determined for certain, but I suspect it was because the temperature in my dressing room, which was very stuffy, rose to about 95°F. Scorpions, though they are inhabitants of hot countries, tend quickly to suffer from heat stress when the thermometer reaches that sort of level.

This February day in 1991 had, until the arrival of the constabulary, been predictably boring. An empty warehouse in a dismal industrial estate on the south bank of the Thames at Woolwich, had been rented for a couple of days by an advertising agency to use as a studio for filming a TV commercial promoting a new brand of cigarettes. They had already shot several other films at other locations with the common theme of having a single white animal among a group of black ones. Thus there was one featuring a white blackbird with a number of black ones, one where a white angel-fish was depicted with a small shoal of black ones and so on. Our purpose today was to film one white, stuffed and painted, leopard with four living black ones.

Black leopards, also known as black panthers, are a common colour variation, but still the same species as the spotted kind. Indeed, black and spotted cubs can be found in the same litter. Black leopards are most frequently encountered in humid, densely forested areas of Indonesia, Burma, Nepal, Assam and southwest China, and less so in tropical Africa. Contrary to popular belief, the black leopard is no fiercer than the spotted form. On this occasion the black leopards had been brought by Jim Clubb, one of the most skilled and reliable of wild animal trainers that I've ever met – and the most humane. It wasn't a difficult shot. A stage had been erected and all the leopards had to do was adopt a variety of positions upon it with good views of their heads. They couldn't give a fig about the presence among them of their deceased, mounted, strangely pallid and unspotted relative.

Directors of still commercial pictures take infinite pains, and thereby spend many hours, in getting every minute detail of position, lighting and expression absolutely right. The crew gathered round the director is of considerable size, and at a bare minimum will comprise an artistic director, a lighting cameraman and his assistant, a camera operator and his assistant, a couple of 'sparks' to handle all things electrical, props men to shift scenery and other objects, painters and carpenters, a runner to fetch and carry anything from tea to cans of unused film, a production secretary to make notes, and usually at least one representative from the advertising agency and another from the production company. They were all there in the warehouse that morning. Plus Jim Clubb and his cats, the caretaker and me. Apart from a couple of small offices and a lavatory there was nothing in the building but the warehouse itself. It was empty except for some hessian-covered bales in one corner and our film set which took up but a small fraction of the available space.

All had gone predictably and, for me tediously, well since we began at eight o'clock. Now it was one o'clock and the director had called a lunch break. With any luck we'd be finished by mid afternoon, for the leopards were performing impeccably. Only the materialization of the massed ranks of the Met led by a man who looked more like a lager lout than a detective inspector, stood between us and the steak and kidney pie.

The director explained who we were and what we were doing.

'Bugger me. And you've really got leopards in there?' said 'Tattered Jeans'. He was relaxing a little.

'Yes. And they detest dogs,' said Jim, who had just joined us. 'I've got them in their crates now, but they can look out through the weld mesh. They'll go wild trying to get at your dogs if you take them anywhere near them.'

'Well, I've got to search the whole building with the dogs.'

'What exactly are you looking for?' I asked.

'Can't say.'

'Couldn't you go everywhere except for the leopards? They don't occupy much space. Your men could visually inspect them but I wouldn't recommend them opening the crates.'

The plainclothes DI talked in whispers to some of the uniformed men. After a few moments he said, 'OK – you can go for lunch, but could your leopard man stay behind to keep an eye on his beasts?'

'Sure,' said Jim. '*If* you'll send a PC across the road to bring me three rounds of tuna sandwiches, wholemeal, and a pint of London Pride.'

'Tattered Jeans' looked as if he was about to be sick. 'Get it, Robinson,' he murmured, mouth like a zipper, and a constable went off muttering.

After a leisurely lunch in the White Horse we all walked back to the warehouse. The place was still seething with policemen and the caretaker was about to be taken away in a police car. Inside the building 'Tattered Jeans' was talking to a small group of plainclothes men gathered in the little office. The atmosphere had changed perceptibly, several were smiling, all seemed content and relaxed, but they at once adopted a more serious expression as we came in. 'Find what you were looking for, gents?' said our director.

'Tattered Jeans' hesitated and then nodded. 'It looks like it,' he said. 'But we've got to ask your animal people a few questions. The bloke back there with the leopards and, I suppose, you if you're involved with them,' he indicated he meant me by waving a hand in my direction. Everyone walked into the main body of the warehouse. Jim sat on a wooden box by the leopard crates reading a newspaper.

'Right,' 'Tattered Jeans' called over to Jim. 'If you wouldn't mind coming over here.' The policemen were keeping well away from the leopards who sat on their haunches, eyes staring, behind their weld mesh grilles. The leopard trainer joined us and 'Tattered Jeans' spoke again. 'It's like this,' he said. 'We found what we were looking for. In spades. But we haven't had a look at your pussy cats yet. We're going to. And I hope you can explain one thing.'

'What's that, for God's sake?' Jim's ruddy moustachioed face wore an expression of complete bewilderment.

'Let's go across – you first please, sir. What we want to look at is the bedding. I assume the leopards are bedded down in their crates?'

En masse, film crew, policemen, Jim and I approached the animals which, on being confronted by this phalanx of humanity, immediately jumped to their feet and began to pace and spit threats. The policemen and film crew stopped in their tracks, but Jim, 'Tattered Jeans' and I moved to within an arm's length of the leopard crates. Jim gentled the cats with soft words. 'Brave Java, good girl. Good girl, Ebony. So there they are,' Jim continued. 'And there's the bedding. Straw. With a little leopard pee and some crap. See, they're emptying their bowels now. You've made them apprehensive. Need some for the station window box?'

'Very funny, sir.' The detective bent down and peered into the crates. He paused for several long seconds. 'But you're right. It's straw.'

'It is indeed straw,' said Jim, his voice heavy with sarcasm. 'Silk sheets are getting a bit expensive these days for bedding down leopards. But the RSPCA say it's OK as second best.'

The detective straightened up and smiled – and it was a genuine smile. 'I'm sorry, gents. I owe you an explanation.

Can't tell you everything, but the gist of it is this. We've found a big, and I mean big, stash of drugs here, while you were in the pub. Did you see some bales over there while you were working this morning?'

I looked. The bales had gone. 'Yes, I remember them,' I said.

'Ecstasy tablets, E, the latest in-drug, specially among the acid house ravers. There was a lot in those bales, I don't know how much yet, possibly as much as half a ton. They have been mixed with other stuff in order to try to fool any cursory inspection by Customs at Dover. Came over from Holland.'

'But what's all this interest of yours in leopard bedding?' asked Jim.

'Those bales you saw were labelled "Pussy Pooper" and contained cat litter, the grey granular stuff you put in a moggy's litter tray. That's what they mixed the Ecstasy with. Little grey tablets among little grey granules.'

'And you wondered if cat litter was also used for big cats,' I said. 'And that maybe there was some connection between Jim being here with his leopards and some dastardly plot to smuggle drugs.'

'Tattered Jeans' smiled and nodded. 'An outside chance, but yes. It turns out to be something of a coincidence. Sorry about all the hassle.'

'Imagine,' said Jim. 'Quite a cover. A circus touring from country to country with drugs in its bales of cat litter. Except no one ever uses cat litter.'

'I can't quite image lions, tigers and leopards squatting house trained over their jumbo-size litter trays,' I said. We all laughed, but I remembered cases in the past where crooks had hidden drugs in waterproof packages placed in the stomachs of camels and, so it was alleged, dolphins, in order to move them across international borders.

The forces of law and order quickly went on their way and we got on with completing the filming. A few months later, as the advertisements featuring the leopards, black and white, began to appear on the hoardings, I read in the newspaper that the villains responsible for the cat litter caper had been sent down for lengthy sentences.

There are stars of the silver screen and then there are *mega* stars, and if Jim Clubb's black leopards are, as I fervently assert, great box office in the glitzy world of feline Thespianism, then Arthur is the Robert de Niro or Tom Cruise of cats. Arthur, of course, is the celebrated white TV cat, advertiser of cat food and particularly notable for the deft way he scoops the contents out of a can with a curled paw.

In summer 1992 I was asked to supervise the animals in a commercial to be filmed at a studio off Charlotte Street in London's West End. Arthur was going to promote a new tinned cat food named after him, and the storyline of the commercial was that he was inviting two of his relatives from overseas to enjoy the delectable repast. The relatives were a pair of lion cubs provided for the filming by a safari park in Northern Ireland. If things went according to plan Arthur would sit before three cans of 'Arthur', scooping away at the central one. In would toddle the two lion cubs and begin eating from the other two cans. It sounded fine, but I imagined all manner of things going wrong. Arthur had apparently never even seen a wild cat before. About to descend upon him now were not one but two who, though cubs, were roughly twice his size. Might he not exit stage left like a feline Baryshnikov performing an appropriate series of rapid *pas de chat*? Might not the lion cubs, big-footed and rather clumsy though delightful creatures, at least put Arthur off his grub? Perhaps cause him to wonder whether these long-lost cousins were about to devour fresh Arthur rather than 'Arthur' in a can? And the cubs were tyros about to make their début before the cameras – might they not refuse to go on stage or perhaps, as had happened during my first television appearance with a lion cub, Simba, that I was nursing at home after operating on its spine in 1967, pass a large and smelly motion centre stage when dazzled by the lights? I resigned myself to a long and frustrating day of innumerable takes.

I had never met Arthur before, and when he arrived at the studio in his comfortable carrying box with his trainer Ann Head, he was treated with all the ceremony that would normally be lavished upon a royal accompanied by a lady in waiting. And what a cool character he proved to be. Stardom hadn't gone to his head in the slightest. There was no trace of the pretentiousness and vanity endemic in human showbiz – just a hint of curiosity in that composed and intelligent face. I could have sworn he was more interested in locating the nearest snack than responding to the admiring remarks of the film crew who gathered round to await his pleasure – an accurate impression as I was later to find out.

The two cubs, presented to him by their keeper who carried one under each arm, seemed pleasantly impressed and stared at Arthur with large round eyes, squeaking softly. Arthur ignored them and washed his face elegantly with a paw. He clearly wanted to get on with the shoot, collect his fee, a considerably bigger one than any of us was receiving, and go home to his fireside.

Mrs Head was worried about him coming into contact with the exotic cats. 'Shouldn't there be a safe disinfectant sprayed on the stage?' she asked me. 'It would be a disaster if Arthur picked anything up from them.'

I felt a trifle niggled that the good lady, an expert on domestic cats rather than wild ones, should cast even the slightest doubt upon the health of the lions. But it was understandable and she was, quite properly, taking maximum precautions on behalf of Arthur, a very valuable 'property' in his own right. 'Don't worry,' I replied. 'The lion cubs are in tip-top health I can assure you. I've just examined them. And what's more, they're vaccinated against everything possible – like Arthur is.'

People often do not realize that the exotic cats in zoos

and wildlife parks are inoculated against the same diseases, such as feline influenza, feline enteritis and so on, using the same vaccines as those administered by vets in general practice. The aim is to protect them from infection brought on to the premises by vagabond cats from the surrounding town or countryside. One of the well-known brands of enteritis vaccine that has been given to hundreds of thousands of pet moggies over the years comprises the inactivated virus strain that was isolated in a British zoo from a snow leopard that died after being infected by a cat which entered the grounds at night in search of food scraps.

After the usual protracted business of brushing every speck of dirt from the matt-black stage, making fine adjustments to the lighting and deciding just where the three tins of cat food were to be positioned, we settled down for the filming. 'Ten-thirty now,' I thought, looking at my watch and slipping *The Magic Flute* into my Walkman. 'No chance of getting anywhere before lunch, all three cats will get fed up with retakes by twelve noon at the latest. *Sashimi* and Kirin beer for lunch downstairs at the Ikkyu, and then a couple of hours of struggle in the afternoon. We might have something in the can by four o'clock.'

First Arthur made his entrance alone. It was a virtuoso solo performance worthy of Gielgud. He sat in front of the three cans, the outer ones of which had their lids left on so that he was obliged to concentrate on the centre. I have known cats with fine appetites, including some of my own, Frank the Siamese among them, but it was immediately apparent that Arthur was a trencherman among cats – a trenchercat, to coin a word. He dug deeply into the meat and lifted it to his mouth, gobbling it down with gusto. It didn't take him many minutes to polish off a whole can, and then sit, four feet neatly together, tail curled elegantly around them, waiting for more. More 'Arthur' was provided. Arthur licked another tin clean. There was not the slightest sign of him baulking, and it wasn't as if he was either an obese or an emaciated individual. He had, still has, an excellent figure of optimum weight. Clearly Arthur relished 'Arthur'.

Now it was time for the entrance of the twin cubs. 'The fun will start here,' I mused, already salivating at the thought of the raw squid and fiery green *wasabi* paste. Lovable as lion cubs are, they can be a bit slow on the uptake. Dare one say it, rather dim?

Lion cubs don't eat cooked canned cat food. Like me with my *sashimi*, they take raw food. Minced meat to be precise. The idea of the commercial, of course, was that Arthur's African cousins would join him in savouring the delights of his eponymous product. A little cheating was called for. The two outer cans were filled with fresh minced steak, while Arthur again had his centre can of 'Arthur'. If all went as planned, Arthur would be sitting there pawing his lunch into his ever open mouth, when in would come the cubs. One would go to the can on his left, the other to the one on his right, and begin scoffing. In the finished version, the voice-over would say something like 'And even his country cousins roar their approval of nourishing new "Arthur".' 'Some hope,' I thought. 'Arthur's perfectly trained. The other two are literally straight out of the Irish bogs.'

'Action!' called the director. Arthur was already eating away – very photogenic. 'Put in the cubs,' the director addressed his command towards the two Irish lion keepers who had brought the young animals over by air. The cubs were set down on one edge of the stage, faces towards Arthur and given gentle shoves on their bottoms. With the typical wobbly, heavy-pawed gait of young lions they padded uncertainly towards our hero.

'He'll be off in a second,' I predicted silently to myself. But Arthur was oblivious to their approach; he had discovered a fresh gastronomic attraction – the raw mince in the other cans.

'Oh my gawd!' I heard a Moschino-suited Sloane from the advertising agency exclaim. 'He's not eating the product!' Sure enough, Arthur was going for the mince as if he hadn't eaten in a month. It still *looked* as if he was eating 'Arthur', of course. The label said so. But he was disrupting the storyline by turning his attentions to the wrong can.

'Cut!' shouted the director. Arthur was the only one to ignore him. He scooped out another pawful of prime mince and raised it to his mouth. The bemused cubs who had barely got beyond the wings were gathered up by the keepers.

After several fruitless attempts to convince Arthur of the indisputable truth that raw meat is unbalanced, unvitaminized, unscientifically concocted, untested, unsterilized and, in a word, un-'Arthur' compared with the marvellous stuff he was being paid to enthuse over, a little of the fresh mince was sprinkled on top of the contents of yet another centre can. The cameras rolled. Arthur tucked in, appetite undiminished, and the cubs were launched once more. They walked over to Arthur. 'Splendid, luvvies,' whispered the director.

'Even if he stays he'll stop eating,' I thought. But Arthur didn't stop eating. To my surprise, the cubs arrived by his side, found their marks, as an actor would say, and began to nuzzle his face. Arthur briefly paused in his chewing to glance at the one on his left and then, incredibly, turned his head and kissed – touched with his nose-tip, tongue slightly protruding – the other, before getting on with the serious business of dining. The cubs, so pleasingly welcomed, sniffed about for a second or two and then began to lick at the meat in their cans. It was a truly wonderful scene – and after a mere handful of takes. So much for my predictions.

'Cut!' yelled the director. 'Fan-bloody-tastic, luvvies. Fan-bloody-tastic! We've got it!'

There was an instant outbreak of kissing, embracing and mutual congratulation among the assembled company. Arthur simply kept on eating. And I went for lunch at the Japanese restaurant. It looked as if I'd got the afternoon off. Never try to second-guess cats, domestic or wild, I thought, as I dipped a piece of squid into the soy sauce. 'I bet Arthur would go a bundle on this.'

Over the past thirty years I've been involved either as presenter or veterinary supervisor in the filming of a large number of lions, other big cats and indeed a broad spectrum of the animal kingdom ranging from butterflies and beetles to whales. But only twice have I had to deal in front of the camera with sloths. These remarkable animals, infrequently exhibited in zoos, come from South America where they form, would you believe, the largest bio-mass, the greatest total weight of animal flesh, in parts of the subcontinent. Despite that, these strange mammals are far less familiar to the man in the street than other South American fauna, such as llamas, jaguars or macaws. Mind you, this may to a large extent be due to the sloths' natural penchant for *not* being noticed. It isn't true, however, that they don't do anything, thus having lent their name to one of the seven deadly sins. In reality, sloths are a very successful species and their success is largely due to the fact that they specialize in feeding on leaves that other animals don't want and living their lives almost entirely hanging upside down in the trees, well out of the way of most predators. Their coats are tinged with green, a useful camouflage, from the presence of algae growing on the hairs; they take up to a month or more to digest a meal of foliage, and they pass urine and droppings but once a week. Slow movers – they travel through the branches at a maximum speed of some quarter-mile per hour – sloths conserve energy by maintaining an unusually low body temperature (86° to 93°F) with the lowest temperatures occurring at night and during rainy weather. Among the South American Indians there is a saying that 'when the wind blows the sloth begins to travel', and a sixteenth-century Spanish colonist wrote of them: 'I have never seen an uglier or more useless creature.' How wrong he was.

In 1988 I had presented a brown-throated three-toed

sloth on 'Number 73', the children's Saturday morning TV programme on which I was resident veterinary surgeon. A placid individual, accustomed to being handled, it had been no trouble at all, and the item was rehearsed and transmitted as planned without a hitch. Quite a different story some seventeen years earlier when I was still living in my home town of Rochdale.

I took the phone call one morning at my then home, a William and Mary stone farmhouse at the foot of the moors that sweep up to become the Pennines' spine separating Lancashire from Yorkshire.

'Doctor Taylor?' said the voice. Posh, Cheshire side of Manchester, I thought. 'My name's Frome, you've probably heard of us. Thirtieth Century Ignox.'

'Sorry, no.'

'Really? Well, TCI happen to be *the* ad agency in the northwest.'

'What can I do for you, Mr Frome?'

'Actually not much, old boy. At least I don't believe so. But it's just to be on the safe side or so I'm advised.'

'What is?'

'Any experience with sloth or sloths, doctor? Not as the old hymn goes "Shake off dull sloth and early rise" and all that, but the animal?'

'I've handled one or two,' I said. The one or two included a sloth in a Norfolk zoo that I had been asked to visit. It hadn't eaten or moved for a couple of months, just hung motionless by its long curved claws from a horizontal branch in its enclosure. The director wasn't unduly worried, but thought it was worth a checkover. I'd gone in to examine it and found it to be a long-dead shell, its viscera entirely eaten away by maggots.

'Thing is,' said Frome. 'We've got one of these beasties lined up for a commercial we're doing. It's for a major car company. The idea is to contrast the sluggard animal with their zippy new convertible model. Clash of images. Get the picture?'

'I see – and you want me to keep an eye on the sloth during filming?'

'Exactly. As I say, I don't think we actually *need* a vet. It's not like a tiger or a wolf, is it? More of a sleepy old do-nothing, from what I hear. But the owners, Wellingborough Zoo, insist that a vet, a zoo vet in fact, be present. It's only a day's filming over at the old airfield at Burtonwood. Can you do it? Twenty-five pounds, say, and lunch.'

'I'll do it. A hundred pounds and lunch.'

The telephone was silent for what seemed like a minute, and then Frome said, 'A hundred pounds. That's a bit steep. You'll have nothing to do in reality. The beastie will simply be filmed hanging upside down from a rail we'll rig up in an old banger. It's not a tiger or wolf,' he repeated.

'A hundred pounds and lunch. You obviously don't know how animals can spring surprises when they're on location. Suppose, for example, it becomes ill. It wouldn't be very good PR if the best you could do was run it down in your nice new motorcar to the PDSA in Warrington. Sloths aren't exactly thick on the ground down the East Lancs Road, you know.'

Frome exhaled noisily. 'All right, then. Seems you've got me by the short and curlies, doc. But I do think it's all rather unnecessary – a personal physician for just one animal. It might as well be the Queen.'

'We know more about the Queen than we do about sloths,' I said. 'Now what are the date and the time you want me?'

It was a bright and sunny April morning when I drove down the M62 to what remained of the old US airbase at Burtonwood. On a length of crumbling tarmac the camera crew and production team were busying themselves around a cluster of vehicles, some the spanking new, soon-to-be-marketed model, others beaten-up old Fords and Renaults overdue for the breakers' yard. Frome, a small ginger-haired young man with a deathly white face and extra-large white ears, introduced himself. He was wearing an eggshell-blue suit. 'Just setting up,' he said chirpily. 'The beastie is in that van over there. Once they've finished fixing up the rail in the Renault, we'll get the chappie who brought it to hang it up and off we go.' He might have been speaking of a suit on a coat-hanger. 'Feel free to wander around the set though, doc.'

'Thanks very much,' I said. It looked like being just another uneventful day. Maybe later I'd get the chance to nip down the motorway to the safari park at Knowsley. But first I decided to have a peek at the sloth to check that it was hail and, so far as these languid creatures can be, hearty. The Wellingborough Zoo keeper opened a large plywood box. Clinging upside down by means of its long curved toenails to a strut spanning the interior was a fully grown female Hoffmann's sloth and not at all ugly. It was in deep slumber – sloths sleep for around nineteen hours out of every twenty-four – and didn't rouse at all when I stroked its dense, hairy coat. I lubricated the plastic-covered wire probe of my electronic thermometer with a blob of saliva and inserted it into the sloth's rectum. The instrument dial registered 87 degrees – only anteaters and armadillos have normal body temperatures as low as sloths. The sloth dreamed on, oblivious to my probings.

'Darlings, would you mind awfully bringing the poor thing on to the set now?'

I helped the keeper carry the box with its sleeping occupant over to the old car which was now illuminated by a semicircle of the lights called 'redheads'. The camera was going to shoot through the open nearside rear door and a rail for the sloth had been fixed over the back seat. Carefully the keeper and I unpicked the sloth's nails from their hold in the box and lifted the animal, now waking and looking slowly round, into the car. We hooked its nails over the rail and it hung there turning its head quizzically from side to side. The director looked through the camera viewfinder. 'No, no, no. It's too far to the left,' he said. 'Could you move it, please?'

The keeper gently took the weight of the sloth with one hand and adjusted the animal's hooked nails with the other. He stood back.

Frome had joined the director and was squinting at the scene through a lens handed to him by the latter. 'Still not anything like right, is it, Dickie?' he said. 'We've got to get it square against the lighting behind it.'

'Do you want me to move it again?' asked the sloth keeper. 'Just say where.'

'The problem,' said the director, 'is its head. I never realized it would be such an odd shape. Can you get it to look to camera?'

The keeper looked nonplussed. 'Not unless it wants to,' he sensibly replied. 'How about me turning it around on the rail?'

Frome gave a squeaky guffaw. 'Leave the arty bit to us, please,' he said. 'If you turned it round it would be looking out of the back window. Quite bizarre. Not what we want.' The whole idea of a sloth in a car, whether looking forward or back, seemed bizarre enough to me.

'Try unbalancing it by taking one foreleg off the rail,' said the director. 'That might make it turn its head slightly.'

The keeper leaned into the car. 'Not the right one, the left,' called Frome. As soon as the left forefoot was unhooked, the sloth slowly and deliberately replaced it once again on the rail, staring fixedly away from the camera. 'Can't you tempt it with some food to look this way?' asked Frome. 'An apple or whatever it eats?'

'It won't eat under these circumstances.'

'Try it!' snapped Frome.

The director was beginning to look somewhat pained. The advertising agency man was still supposed to be there on a watching brief. The director directed the show. The keeper fished in a bag and produced a stick of celery which he proferred to the sloth. 'It's her favourite snack,' he muttered. The sloth wouldn't touch it.

'Bloody stupid animal,' Frome's voice grated again. 'Look, I'll show you what we want.' He pushed the keeper out of the way and crouched on the edge of the car's back seat. 'Come on, dopey,' he said, reaching towards the sloth with both hands.

'Look, sloths aren't . . .' The keeper didn't finish his sentence.

Frome cut him off with 'This animal's been paid for to do the job right. OK?' He seized the sloth round its chest and began to pull.

'That's *not* the way to handle . . .' I interrupted, but it was too late.

Sloths may look like defenceless dimwits. Not so. The green algae on their coat acts as camouflage against marauding harpy eagles, the dense and tough skin, and ability to curl up into a very tight ball, give added protection. But there is something else, that the sloth at that moment elected to demonstrate. Voluntarily detaching one forefoot from the rail, it swept the two powerful, sickle-shaped nails across Frome's chest in one measured and steady movement. There was the crisp sound of a shirt ripping, the pop of jacket buttons and then a piercing wail from Frome. He sprang backwards in the confined space, clutching at the sloth and banging his head hard on the inside of the doorframe. The sloth fell on to the floor of the vehicle with a thud and sprawled there. Frome's ankle was close to its jaws – so it promptly bit him, and because it was a Hoffmann's sloth, the sort that has a large molar tooth set well forward in the jaw, it went deep. Frome wailed again. He extricated himself from the car and turned towards the startled film crew. Two crimson slashes were dripping blood behind the tattered remains of his shirt and he stood on one leg while more blood seeped through the sock of the other. 'Look! Look! The thing's gone mad,' he croaked and then, with a frightened glance over his shoulder, began hobbling towards us. The sloth, more or less helpless as sloths are when they find themselves on the ground, squirmed awkwardly where it had fallen. I didn't like the way it had crashed so heavily to the floor and ran over to examine it. Cautiously I lifted it out, laid it on the tarmac and began running my fingertips over its bones.

'Bloody hell! That's about the limit!' Frome's voice was almost a shriek. 'Look at him. Fussing over the bloody animal. What about me? I've been *savaged*! Do you know, *savaged*!'

Luckily the sloth hadn't suffered any injury. It was more alarmed than anything else. I gave it a small injection of Valium. Behind me Frome groaned loudly as folk took off his shirt and sock and someone went to a car for a first-aid kit. 'Oh my God!' he moaned. 'Get me to hospital. That bloody vet can't think of anything but his godforsaken monster.'

With the sloth safely back in its box I went to have a look at Frome, who was now babbling on about the possibility of being infected with rabies. His wounds weren't serious but it was best for him to go to the nearest casualty department for a precautionary tetanus shot. 'For God's sake, put some antibiotic on to my wounds *now*,' he bleated while he was helped into the car that would run him to the hospital. 'I might be going septic already.'

So I sprayed his two chest rakes and the hole in his ankle with my purple-coloured Tervamycin spray. As he was driven away I could hear him protesting loudly about the deep purple stains where some of the spray had fallen on his eggshell-blue suit.

'Never work with animals or kids. Isn't that the first rule of the acting profession?' I said to the director after he'd gone.

He grinned and said, 'Now, shall we try again?'

After resting for a couple of hours the sloth put on an inspired performance of immobility exactly where the director wanted her. We were all finished and packing up by the time Frome returned from the hospital. He was restored to his cocky self again. 'The doctors were most impressed,' he said proudly. 'They'd never seen a sloth bite before. Quite made their day.'

'Made ours too,' said the keeper from Wellingborough Zoo softly.

7

Fearsome Fangs

Now the serpent was more subtle than any beast of the field . . .

Genesis 3:1

All men carry about them that which is poison to serpents:
for it be true that is reported, they will no better abide the
touching with man's spittle than scalding water cast upon
them: but if it happens to light within their jaws or
mouth, especially if it comes from a man that is fasting, it is
present death.

Pliny, *Historia Naturalis* Book vii, ch. 2

Pliny the Elder, that illustrious Roman polymath of the first
century AD, has left us thirty-seven tomes on all aspects of
natural history. Unfortunately the four volumes devoted to
zoology contain much from the world of fantasy. Tales of
mouthless men whose only food source was the perfumes of
flowers and fruits; of the Sciapodae or Umbrella-foots,' a
people who used their enormous feet as parasols for
protection against the sun; of winged horses and unicorns.

Likewise his account quoted above, of the dire effects of
human saliva upon snakes, is just so much delicious
bunkum. Spitting cobras exist and deadly beasts they are,
but spitting *on* cobras, something I would advise you
against, because of the close proximity necessary for
accurate expectoration of your gob of spittle, won't do it
the slightest harm. It may, however, irritate it — does
anyone really relish being spat upon? And irritated cobras
or other species of venomous snake are best avoided.
During my career I have had to confront more than a few
very irritable snakes, some of which had indisputably lost
all of their gruntle!

There is some debate among experts as to which is the most dangerous snake in the world. Five of the leading authorities on such matters were asked to give their 'ten most dangerous' list. The results of this survey placed the following species in descending order of malignancy: king cobra, taipan, mamba, bush master, tiger snake, common cobra, puff adder, Russell's viper, sawscaled viper and jararacussu – a pit viper from Brazil. Only the king cobra appeared in the list of every expert.

All the species mentioned are ones that live on land. In the sea, however, there also dwell very dangerous snakes, and one of these, the yellow-bellied sea snake is the most widely distributed of all the world's reptiles. Sea snake venom must rank as possibly the most toxic of all, but since the animals are generally docile and not at all quick tempered, the risk to humans when coming into contact with them is usually far less than with some of the snakes in the above league table of notoriety and which are, by nature, more aggressive and irascible.

Sea snakes, of which there exist some fifty kinds, all live in the warm coastal waters of the Western Pacific and Indian oceans, with the exceptions of one freshwater species and the aforementioned yellow-bellied sea snake whose range extends from East Africa to the west coast of South America, and from Australia to southern Siberia. They are seldom displayed in aquaria, though I remember some in a heated pool at Belle Vue Zoo, when I was a small boy. Apart from those, the first time I came face to face with a sea snake was in 1973 when I was swimming in Singapore, and watched a four-foot long yellow sea snake with dark bands on its upper surface that was drifting in mid water, suddenly strike at, instantly kill, and swallow head first, a small squaretail fish. I identified it later as a Stoke's sea snake, and read that a giant gathering of millions of individuals of this species, some ten feet wide and over sixty miles long has been recorded moving slowly through the water between Malaysia and Sumatra.

A few years later I was in Hong Kong to visit Ocean Park. A serious epidemic of melioidosis, a very dangerous bacterial disease that had been carried by wind and rain from contaminated soil in the region around China's Pearl River, killing many of the park's marine mammals, was being brought under control with the help of a vaccine we'd had specially prepared at the Pasteur Institute in Paris.

Paw Ket, the veterinary paramedic at Ocean Park's Animal Clinic, invited me to go sailing for the afternoon. Following a lunch on the Jumbo Floating Restaurant of pigs' small intestines and spleens (his choice when I asked him to order his idea of a Chinese slap-up meal), we took a launch across Aberdeen Harbour and pulled up alongside a small fishing boat. It was an old and sun-bleached twenty-foot scow that had long been in need of repainting, and was fitted out with an inboard engine covered by a tea box and a flimsy roof of rattan at the stern shading a seat by the tiller. 'This is my brother-in-law, Tong Fat,' said Paw Ket introducing me to a young man of perhaps twenty in white shorts and T-shirt who was squatting in the well of the boat arranging a pile of fishing net with a perky little black and white dog, resembling a Lancashire heeler, sitting beside him.

Tong Fat jumped to his feet smiling and pointed to the dog. 'And this is Star,' he said as we shook hands. 'Make yourselves comfortable and the four of us will go fishing.' We stepped aboard. Tong Fat lifted the tea box cover, fiddled within and presently the engine putt-putted into life. As we nosed slowly out between the rows of sampans, the smells of roast meat, herbs, garlic and fish mixed in with that of sewage and engine oil in the humid air, Star took up what was obviously his habitual crew station at the front of the boat. With his forepaws neatly perched on the prow, and gazing bright-eyed into the distance, he made a most cheerful figurehead.

We left the jungle of skyscrapers, the bustling wharves and waterfront hotels, the floating slums and the back-

The deadly yellow-bellied sea snake.
(Anthony Bannister/NPHA)

The not-so-sluggish sloth. *(Wardene Weisser/Ardea)*

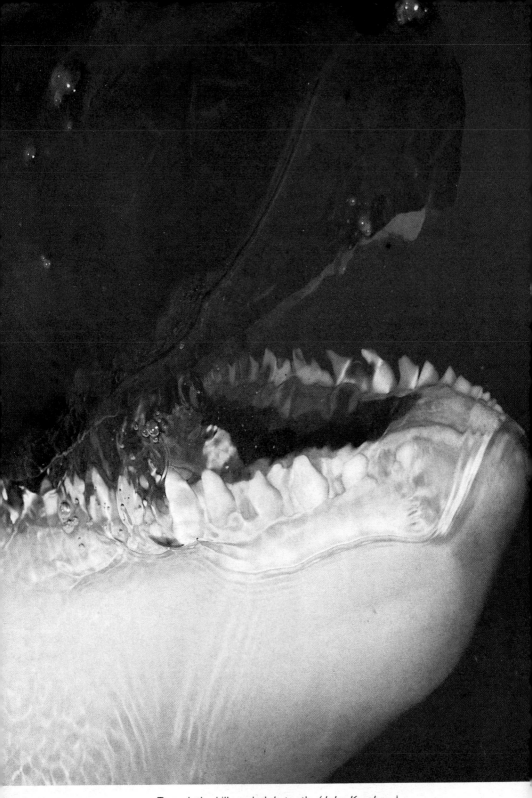

Tanouk the killer whale's teeth. *(John Kershaw)*

With Bruce Walton, inspecting Tanouk before the dentistry. *(John Kershaw)*

Peter Kertesz sets up his drilling equipment while Tanouk looks on. *(John Kershaw)*

Leopard cubs and chimpanzees are cuddly – at this age! *(David Taylor)*

ground of green hills behind us in the grey haze as we chugged out towards the islands. We passed a single old-style junk, its sails the colour of dried blood, making for Kowloon, and watched as a couple of frogmen hauled a corpse on to the deck of a police launch. Tong Fat handed out cold Tsing Tao beers that he produced from a plastic cool box. Star barked occasionally at gulls that swooped too close to his vessel and I sat on the seat next to Paw Ket who was steering and looked forward with pleasant anticipation to an afternoon's fishing for bonito. It was their breeding season; they would be close inshore. Paw Ket had provided me with a reel and line, and a bucket of smelly squid bits for bait was as far away as possible in the bows. 'You can line-fish, doctor,' said Paw Ket. 'But Tong Fat will use his circular net. He is most skilled at casting it.'

We had sailed for half an hour under a sky of silver, the sun's glare diffused in the haze, when we arrived at an inlet in the shoreline of a low bush-covered island. It was on the far side, with Hong Kong and the mainland of China hidden from view. Star left his post as soon as the engine was killed and walked back towards me, wagging his tail. He was clearly ready for the fun. It was a peaceful anchorage with no sounds save that of the water lapping against the boat, yet the teeming millions of Hong Kong were but a few miles away.

'Here is a fine place for groupers and snappers,' said Tong Fat. He busied with his net and I attached lumps of squid to my line hooks. Paw Ket opened more cans of Tsing Tao, and Star just stood wagging his tail furiously.

Tong Fat went for'ard, folds of net over one shoulder. He stood for a few minutes at the prow looking down at the water and then, with a graceful sweep of an arm, cast out his net. It spun open as it flew through the air and landed on the water surface as an almost perfect circle, connected to Tong Fat by a long cord that he held in a hand. The net disappeared from view quickly as it sank, but reappeared after a few seconds as the young man hauled it in. Caught in its mesh were a handful of small red and shining silver fishes. Tong Fat shook them out on to the decking and Star bustled about excitedly inspecting them, but not once attempting to bite any. Tong Fat gathered the net together, arranged its loops and folds once more, and then cast again. It looked easier than it was to drop the revolving circle of netting precisely where the fisherman wanted. I tried it once and the two Chinese laughed good-naturedly and slapped me on the back when it became entangled with my head at the moment of casting. Star joined in the mirth by jumping up and down merrily and barking. Tong Fat cast again and again from the prow with little success. Eventually he decided to try over the side of the boat, and this time when he pulled it in, the net was in the form of a bag, bulging with a flickering tumult of metallic-scaled fish of many colours from which the water streamed in glistening cascades. Paw Ket went to help him heave the net over the gunwales and spill out its jiggling contents. Star was trying his best to assist in some way.

The decking of the small boat became a gleaming, shimmering patchwork of colour. 'Right, let's see what we have here,' said Tong Fat. 'We'll throw back the ones that are not for eating.' He pointed at a mustard-yellow fish flapping close to my foot. 'Put that over the side, doctor,' he said. 'It's a black-spotted puffer – quite poisonous. And there's a young castor-oil fish.' He indicated one, blue-grey in colour. 'I don't normally catch these in shallow water during the daytime. Eat that and it will purge your bowels. Hence the name.'

As he bent down to take hold of the castor-oil fish to throw it overboard, Star pitched forwards without making a sound on to the carpet of struggling fish. 'My God, what are you up to?' murmured Tong Fat. The little dog didn't respond but simply lay in a heap, trembling slightly, while fins flapped against his body and fish-mouths gaped, as if in amazement.

I kneeled down and touched Star. I put my hand to his

head and delicately flipped the cornea of one eye. No blink. I felt on the inside of his hind leg for his femoral artery. No pulse. Star was dead.

My companions were dumbstruck. It was after some minutes of staring with unbelieving eyes at the motionless body that Tong Fat said in a whisper, 'It cannot be. He was only three years old. As healthy as a young lion.'

Paw Ket gasped and shouted something in Cantonese. His brother-in-law whirled around and grabbed a large knife jutting from a slot in one of the boat's timbers. 'Look out, doctor!' he exclaimed in English. 'Stand back!' With a lightning stroke of the knife blade, he slashed at something lying among the scattered fish. It writhed violently as its head was severed cleanly from its body. At first I took it to be one of those pretty tropical eels. The creature was about two feet long with a sinuous body, gleaming black on the upper surface and pale yellow below. Its detached head was finely tapered. In fact, it was a yellow-bellied sea snake, one drop of whose venom is powerful enough to kill three adult men.

I lifted up poor Star's corpse and inspected it carefully, parting his short coat with my fingers. It took me almost a quarter of an hour to find them – two fine puncture points on the side of a forepaw. The holes were as tiny as those made by a hypodermic needle of the gauge I use on parrots and smaller birds. So that was it – Star must have stepped on the sea snake as it lay among the fish on the decking. It had reacted by biting him. Star almost certainly didn't feel a thing. Humans report that the bite of a sea snake is virtually painless, and the absorption of the poison is so rapid that in many instances there is no time even for first aid.

Tong Fat took the boat closer inshore, jumped in the water and then waded on to the beach carrying Star's body. He buried his pet under a bush, digging the grave with his knife.

We threw all the fish – and the remains of the sea snake – into the sea, and without another word passing between us, sailed back to Hong Kong. To this day Tong Fat visits the island each year on the anniversary of Star's death and burns joss-sticks at his grave.

No one knows for sure how many human beings die from sea snake bites each year in the Indo-Pacific region. They may well account for some fishermen who simply never return from a trip out to sea. Certainly the animals are frequently caught up in nets and occasionally on hook and line. Bathers may step on the snakes in shallow, turbid water such as is found at river mouths, places where sea snakes like to congregate, and some estimates suggest that there is around one sea snake bite per two hundred and seventy thousand human-bathing hours in some tropical waters such as those around Malaysia. As for dogs that sail as their masters' shipmates, who can tell?

Talking of snakes and dogs brings to mind another of my cases when I was first working at Belle Vue Zoo in Manchester.

'PC Schofield, Smallbridge Police,' said the voice on the telephone. 'We've got an emergency and a right rum one at that. Dog swallowed by snake. The snake will be on its way to your place with a police escort in two ticks. Could you be ready for it, sir?'

I had just arrived home from the surgery, tired and ready for lunch. The fish pie was on the table and Casals was playing on the Third Programme. Thirty seconds after I'd put down the telephone I was back in the car and driving down the lane towards Rochdale. Dog swallowed by snake. Not likely to be a joke – the voice had authentic constabulary style I was sure. Snakes of the constrictor sort, pythons, anacondas and the like, are not venomous, but kill their prey by suffocating and biting before swallowing it whole. Big specimens of constrictor species can take pigs, goats or gazelles, and dogs would present no difficulties for their engulfing jaws. There is even a handful of authenticated cases of people, admittedly children or small adults, being swallowed. But the biggest individuals of Britain's native species could not tackle anything bigger than a mouse or a frog. So it must be an exotic species of constrictor, and a sizeable one, I decided, that was being escorted to the braying of sirens and the flashing of blue lights. I pressed down on the accelerator. What was good enough for a snake would surely provide the snake doctor with a cast-iron excuse if I was pulled up for speeding through the town centre.

I drew up behind a police car parked outside the surgery on Milnrow Road. The caretaker had let the visitors in. Walking down the passageway, I at once caught the sound of loud voices coming from the waiting room. Inside the room were four people – PC Schofield, who quickly introduced himself, a policewoman and two civilians who were arguing fiercely. I recognized them as Mr and Mrs Smallbone, clients of mine. He was short, fat and red-faced with a droopy black moustache. She was short, fat and red-faced with tightly curled blonde hair and a wide, thin-lipped mouth. They ran a fish and chip shop famed for tasty rag puddings, homemade by Mrs Smallbone. The latter was also a breeder of pedigree dogs – papillons, not often to be found in Lancashire in those days, and her husband was a fanatical amateur herpetologist, who kept a small collection of non-venomous snakes in a greenhouse in their back garden. I had been called to treat both dogs and snakes on several occasions in the past, sometimes bringing home a brace of rag puddings for the family.

As I entered, the Smallbones interrupted their heated exchange and glared at me. PC Schofield gave a loud sigh of relief and explained, 'It's in there, doc.' He nodded towards a large sack lying in the middle of the waiting room. 'The snake wot swallowed the dog. We were called to a domestic dispute and . . .'

Mrs Smallbone at this point burst into tears and rushed over to me. 'You've got to get crackin' *now* and I mean *now*. Come on!' Her voice rose to a wail. 'Gerrit out! Get my darlin' Candy out!'

Mr Smallbone groaned. 'Hold on a minute, woman. He don't know wot happened yet!'

'I bloody do!' howled his wife. 'Your bloody snake ate 'er, that's wot, and you wouldn't gerrer out.'

'Please calm down, everyone,' I shouted and picked up the sack. It was heavy – PC Schofield had to give me a hand. 'Let's go into the surgery.' The others followed us, the Smallbones arguing still, as the policeman and I went through the door carrying the sack between us.

Smallbone was purple-faced with anger as we gathered round the examination table and I began untying the knotted cord round the neck of the sack. '*She* wanted me, there and then, to chop off Sammy's head with a meat cleaver. I mean, what would have been the point, eh? Killin' Sammy for what? Nowt we could have done for the dog then!'

'Resuscitation! Re-bloody-suscitation! That's wot,' screamed his wife. 'There's still hope. If the vet here will get his finger out.'

Mr West, the caretaker, put his head round the surgery door. His wife in their flat upstairs was getting alarmed by all the noise.

The sack flopped open to reveal a magnificent reticulated python, one of a species that is native to tropical Asia. I grasped its head, holding the jaws shut (though non-venomous, the fangs of such a beast are sharp and long and, as I knew from bitter experience, can inflict a bad bite that easily becomes infected) and began to withdraw the powerful, muscular body. It must have been at least twelve feet long. The snake squirmed slowly on the table top. 'That's Sammy!' said Smallbone, a distinct hint of pride in his voice.

'And that's Candy!' spluttered Mrs Smallbone through a new deluge of tears. She pointed a trembling finger towards a large lump distorting the smooth lines of the reptile about two feet behind its head. 'There must be a chance! Please,

please get Candy out!' she caught hold of my sleeve and tugged urgently. 'Open him up!'

Later it transpired that *someone* – one of several points of dispute between the couple – had neglected to ensure that the door of the greenhouse in their back garden was properly closed. Candy, a best-of-breed two years running at Manchester Dog Show, and soon-to-be Crufts competitor, had wandered into the greenhouse where Sammy, given the run (or perhaps I should say, given the slither) of the cosily warm building while other, smaller serpents occupied a number of vivaria on the floor, was lying coiled on a shelf more commonly used to support pots of tomato plants. Sammy was becoming rather peckish, it was after all three weeks since his last feed of dead rabbit. His flicking tongue 'smelled' Candy's presence as soon as she came in. Thirty seconds later his double-hinged jaws, aided by the mouthful of sickle-shaped teeth began, with slow, steady gulps, inexorably to propel the papillon's warm body down Sammy's elastic throat. Candy's pretty little hind feet were just disappearing as a horrified Mrs Smallbone happened to glance through one of the panes of glass in the greenhouse door while pegging out some washing. Her screams brought Mr Smallbone, who was at the time busy serving rag puddings, fish, chips and mushy peas to the brisk lunchtime trade, running and puffing into the back garden.

The row that ensued centred on Mrs Smallbone's demand that Sammy be executed without delay and the ingested, and hopefully still living, best-of-breed extricated by a swift slash of a knife. Mr Smallbone took a different view. Fond as he was of the now almost departed – toenails still visible – Candy, he was inclined to believe that the papillon was indisputably and irreversibly a 'goner' as he put it. That being the case, what was the point of snuffing out his beloved Sammy, the most beautiful four yards of reticulated python to be found in Lancashire outside the reptile house at Belle Vue Zoo?

Actions speaking louder than even Mrs Smallbone's

words, she promptly stormed off to the potting shed and returned in a trice with a cleaver and a pruning knife. 'Kill the bugger now!' she had yelled succintly while waving the weapons under her spouse's nose, and attracting the attention of a next-door neighbour who took one peep over the wooden fence before scurrying indoors to dial 999. Which is when PC Schofield and his colleague became involved.

'Is there any chance that the dog is still alive?' asked the policeman as I ran my fingers over the lump that was Candy, or more precisely, Candy in a snakeskin coat. 'It's about twenty-five minutes since it happened.'

'There's no air down there,' muttered Smallbone glumly.

'How do you know, arsehole?' barked his wife, looking at him with meditated murder in her eyes. 'There's stories in't papers every day of folk surviving when they've been given up for dead.' Then she began yelling again, demanding that I operate on the snake *pronto*, xxxxing-well get on with it, is what she actually advised.

'Could you open Sammy up – without killing him?' asked Smallbone, his voice quiet though exasperated, and his face purpling again.

'I can give him an anaesthetic and do a gastrotomy,' I answered. 'But there are the usual risks. As for the dog, it's almost certainly been dead for almost half an hour. Don't forget Sammy didn't just swallow him, he bit him first.' I opened the snake's jaws to display the array of teeth. Sammy did not struggle. He was enjoying an after-lunch doze.

'Do it!' said both the Smallbones in perfect unison. At least they agreed on that.

I wheeled over the anaesthetic machine. Halothane vapour was the best and safest anaesthetic for snakes at that time. Placing a funnel-shaped rubber mask over Sammy's face, I turned on the oxygen and adjusted the halothane flow meter. Snakes breathe very slowly, and so it took some five minutes before the python was relaxed and unconscious. During that induction time I assembled a selection of instruments and sterile drapes, while the Smallbones, though less voluble now, kept up a steady exchange of fire, and the police stood silently looking on.

I made the incision through the scales of Sammy's belly where there is only a thin layer of muscle. Another cut through the stomach wall, and there was Candy – dead as a doornail – her once silky coat plastered flat with digestive mucus.

'Oh, my baby!' Mrs Smallbone's howl made bottles on a nearby shelf tinkle as they vibrated. 'Can't you give 'er mouth to mouth?'

The policewoman put an arm around her. 'It's no use, luv, it's all over,' she said gently. It was just like a scene from 'The Bill' or 'Casualty'. Mr Smallbone watched fixedly as if in a trance, while I sutured the incision. His face, its usual red again, was beaded with sweat. Sammy came round quickly after I switched off the gas machine.

'Bring him in to have the stitches removed in a fortnight,' I said as I helped Smallbone slide his python back into the sack. He didn't hear me, so absorbed was he in his pet's condition.

'We'll run you back in the car,' said PC Schofield, rather generously I thought.

'You can take 'im and that bloody snake,' replied Mrs Smallbone, venom tingeing her sobs. 'I'm going with Candy in a taxi. And 'im and me's *finished*!' She made a V sign with two fingers towards her husband.

A little while later, after the police car had taken Smallbone and his snake back to Smallbridge, Mrs Smallbone climbed into the taxi I had ordered for her, with a plastic bag containing Candy's corpse cradled in her arms. 'Thanks, doc,' she whispered as I was closing the taxi door. 'But you mark my words, she'd have won at Crufts. I'll divorce that bastard Smallbone over this!' Six months later I read in the *Rochdale Observer* that she did do just that.

Sammy recovered from his operation uneventfully, per- haps wondering why he felt hungry so soon after his last meal, and was shortly scoffing rabbits rather than papillons once again. The last time I saw him he had grown to almost eighteen feet.

Star and Candy cannot be described as two of my cases of snake treatment, more as ones of canine non-treatment that came to rapidly fatal conclusions. To counter any impression I may be giving that I have an unfortunate habit of arriving too late in all circumstances where snakes, venomous or not, are involved, I must assure you that I do, and always have since I became a zoo vet, treat snakes' *own* ailments and injuries quite frequently.

No less than mammals and birds, snakes and other reptiles are heir to all manner of diseases, most of them uninvestigated by scientists, not least because there is little money available for research into such creatures. Also, it must be said that mammals and birds are more popular, evoke more affection, with the majority of people, vets included, than rhinoceros iguanas, mugger crocodiles and death adders. I admit death adders aren't for cuddling, won't peck seed out of your hand, don't grace your lawn, can't give you a ride or pull a cart, and probably wouldn't taste too good even if prepared by the Roux brothers (yes, I know lots of people in the USA say rattlesnake meat is better than chicken, and that the Japanese eat sea snakes). But even though I admit all that, I still think snakes are wonderful, brilliantly designed creatures, elegant, svelte, even when of awesome size or possessing deadly poison, with a history stretching back long before man made his entrance on the world's stage, and playing a most useful role in the scheme of things as specialist predators. One can love snakes even though snakes are not *lovable*.

I don't see many snakes during the course of my work, in comparison with the numbers of mammals and birds on my patient list. One reason is that with the exception of very big specimens of snakes and crocodiles, and certain rare species such as komodo dragons, they aren't worth very much in financial terms. Owners, both private and in zoos, do not generally want to spend much money on diagnosis and treatment, let alone the expense of flying people like me in to examine them. It's a different story for elephants, giraffes and dolphins, of course, but a blood test or an X-ray for a twelve-inch-long rat snake bought for five pounds from a pet shop costs no less than one for a baby giant panda.

Another reason is that reptiles frequently don't show much in the way of symptoms when they fall ill. Some species quite naturally go many days between feeds. Snakes will commonly give up eating altogether if for some, perhaps subtle, reason, they are not happy with their surroundings. Psychological anorexia occurs among serpents as well as royal princesses. By the time keepers notice significant weight loss, the disease may be well advanced, even terminal. Routine health checks, including full blood analysis are seldom performed on snakes.

And then there's the lethal factor. Many keepers of snakes understandably handle venomous species as little as possible. If one falls sick, it may become even more ill-tempered than usual – why risk a bite and its potential consequences? The treatment of snake bite by injection of antiserum, especially in the hands of an inexperienced casualty department, can in some cases make a person even sicker than if they'd been left untreated. So I suspect that many venomous snakes are left to the mercy of God when they are out of sorts and, as is the way with most illnesses in both man and beast, they cure themselves.

Nevertheless I am called upon from time to time to come to grips with a venomous snake, and I'm always apprehensive and occasionally downright scared, as when a man mishandled a spitting cobra he was showing me while my daughter, Stephanie, then only about ten years old, was in the room. A crotchety snake that can send a jet of venom into the eyes with accuracy up to a distance of about nine feet, the spitting cobra reared into its attack posture after being so unceremoniously dropped upon the floor. I grabbed Stephanie, pushed her behind me and turned my face away from the snake. Luckily the owner of the reptile quickly retrieved it and secured it again in the rubber-padded jaws of his snake tongs. Nowadays I always wear goggles or a plastic visor when dealing with spitting cobras, but I still feel embarrassed at being such a fool when Stephanie reminds me, once in a while, of the time I took her, unprotected, into the presence of one of the snakes that I fear most of all.

The Gaboon viper is a stocky, attractively marked snake with a massive head and fangs that can be two inches long. When it bites it bites deep, injecting a formidable quantity of venom, and can thus kill a man unusually quickly. Fortunately it is also one of the most docile and agreeable of serpents, and bites (of humans) are rare.

While visiting the Madrid Zoo in 1991 I was asked by the curator of reptiles to take a look at a Gaboon viper in the zoo's excellent collection of venomous snakes. He suspected it was showing signs of 'mouth rot', one of the commonest ailments of snakes and some other reptiles, and one that is often difficult to eradicate. For some years, on and off, my veterinary colleagues at Madrid Zoo and I had been struggling to control persistent 'mouth rot' in their precious female komodo dragon, and fighting what I was beginning to fear was a losing battle. 'Mouth rot' or stomatitis is one of my least favourite diseases. It is caused by several kinds of bacteria that invade abrasions in the lining of the mouth, and can easily progress to enteritis, pneumonia or blood poisoning, often with a fatal outcome.

The curator took me into the Fauna Africana where the snake exhibition is housed, and showed me the handsome snake lying coiled in the sand of its vivarium. 'I'll get it out,' he said. 'So you can see the mouth.'

As ever, I was somewhat apprehensive at once again having to work at the dangerous end of such a snake. '*Muy bien*,' I replied. 'Grab it and then hold it tight behind the head and press firmly down on the table here. Are you going to use the tongs?'

'No. Gaboons are so strong. I'll feel happier using my hands.' Some zoos have systems whereby dangerous snakes can be cooled and so made torpid for handling. Not so in Madrid.

The curator turned his key in the lock of the vivarium and opened the plastic window. He paused for an instant and then, with both hands, seized the viper by its neck. It thrashed wildly as he brought it out and laid it on the table; that cut down its ability to throw its body about.

'Here I go,' I said, and with a pair of closed scissors, teased open the snake's jaws, bringing the gums and enormous fangs into view. There was no doubt about it – 'mouth rot' had set in. The gums were swollen, red and ulcerated at the front of the mouth. At that moment the curator sneezed the mother of all sneezes – *and lost his grip on the snake*. The Gaboon viper, its fangs an inch away from my hand, its head free to move, its eyes looking icily at my fingers, opened its jaws wide.

I froze. Fear, like a cold alpine stream, coursed through my brain. Now for the deep bite, the jets of poison, the end. The viper looked at my finger, long fangs poised to strike, mouth fully agape. And then, astoundingly and slowly it closed it. Time, which had stood still, began moving once more. I snatched my hand away as the curator grabbed the snake again and bundled it back into the vivarium. 'Phew, I'm so sorry, doctor,' said the curator. 'It was some fine sand up my nose.'

'That's OK,' I said, not meaning a word of it. 'It *is* "mouth rot".'

'And what do you suggest?'

'First, a large cognac. On you. And then I'll go over a treatment course of antibiotics and hydrogen peroxide mouthwashes with you.'

It felt great to be alive as we both walked out of the

Fauna Africana into the crisp autumn air, the sunlight streaming through the trees of the Casa de Campo, turning them into showers of gold coins. 'Shakespeare got it right in his poem *The Rape of Lucrece*, I mused as we passed the lawn where one of the pandas, Chang-Chang, was sitting with a branch of bamboo in his paws. ' "Who sees the lurking serpent steps aside" – give me giant pandas or tigers or killer whales any time.'

8

In at the Birth

I received a letter from a distinguished member of the
profession asking me whether, in my opinion, I thought it
possible for a woman to give birth to a dog.

Dr G M Gould MD, in *Anomalies and Curiosities of
Medicine*, 1896

The man on the telephone had clearly been most excited –
and absolutely certain about what had happened. 'Doctor,
come at once. The gemsbok calf has been born but ten
minutes and there is a most poisonous snake clinging to its
nose. You must kill it and take it off!' So now I was driving
up the sand-swept road towards Dubai staring intently
along the beams of my headlights, alert for the first glimpse
of that common cause of accidents in the Emirates – a
camel sitting in the darkness, enjoying the day's heat that
was retained in the asphalt. Apart from doing considerable
damage to camel and vehicle, collisions with the resting
beasts, no matter how far from human habitation they
might appear to be, would surely be followed within
seconds by the materialization from nowhere of a stick-
waving bedou claiming ownership and demanding recom-
pense at once in the form of several thousand dirhams.

It was September 1983 and I was replacing my assistant,
Chris Furley, as resident vet at Al Ain Zoo in Abu Dhabi
Emirate while he was on leave. As well as looking after the
health of the vast collection of animals at Al Ain, we were
regularly called to the animal collections of Sheikh Zayd,
the ruler, and those of other sheikhs both in Abu Dhabi and
elsewhere in the Gulf. My destination on this occasion was

the depressing old zoo in Dubai – little more than a few acres of back garden attached to a villa.

If the Pakistani who had called me hadn't been so insistent as to what had occurred, I would have waited until the following sunrise to make the two-and-a-half-hour journey from the inland oasis of Al Ain to Dubai on the coast. But there had been no doubt in his mind, he had been there, witnessed it! 'The snake entered the gemsbok mother's womb while she was still pregnant,' he had explained. 'We have so many snakes – sand snakes, sawscale vipers, in the garden – and I, Faisal, was there in the paddock when the gemsbok gave birth. The snake, already clinging like a vampire to the calf, was upon it when it first came into the world! It is something I have heard of, doctor, but never seen – until today!'

As the first dim glow from the city lights of Dubai became visible in the distance, I considered what I might find when I got to the gemsbok calf. There had been a recent claim from somewhere in Asia of a woman who had swallowed a snake's egg which had subsequently hatched in her stomach, the emerging baby reptile surviving and being audible as it moved about. The woman, according to the account I'd read, had been sent to Spain for surgery, presumably a gastrotomy. Intrigued by the story I tried to trace the case, if it existed, to discover exactly what it might be, in the Spanish press – but to no avail. And I recalled that the great sixteenth-century French physician, Ambroise Paré wrote of a woman in Krakovia who in 1494 gave birth 'to a dead baby which had attached to its back a live serpent, which had gnawed it to death'. Paré had even made a drawing of the foetus and serpent, a copy of which I possessed. 'Hmmmm, and now a gemsbok,' I mused as I crossed the creek and entered the city. 'I wonder.'

Certainly there are snakes aplenty in the countries bordering the Gulf. We frequently saw them in the zoo's great paddocks at Al Ain and occasionally I had been called by Tawam Hospital to identify a snake that had bitten a patient – usually a bedou from the desert. Although the bedouin consider all desert reptiles – including the harmless lizards – to be poisonous, the commonest venomous snake by far is the sawscaled viper. This snake is one which I treat with the utmost respect, for many experts consider it to be one of the most dangerous species on account of its powerful venom and aggressiveness. Apart from the few dogs which I treated for snake bites when I was in general practice – usually when they had been away with their owners on holiday in Devon or Cornwall during hot summers – I hadn't much experience of snakes biting animals. There had been a very few cases of zebras and antelope in Middle Eastern zoos where I had suspected snake bite as the cause of death – but there had been no facilities available to prove it one way or the other. Overall I'd seen far more snake bites on humans, including myself, than on any other species.

As I pulled up outside the zoo's entrance, the Pakistani curator, who must have been waiting for me in the shadows, at once came hurrying over and switched on a torch. 'Ah, good evening, doctor, welcome, thank you for coming – this way, please, no time to lose.' He took my black bag, slung it over his shoulder and ushered me impatiently through the gateway. 'It is still attached to the poor calf. Still sucking. But yet the calf lives.' We came to the fencing of a small paddock and the curator raked his torch beam from side to side searching for my patient. The light came to rest on the black and white mask of a female gemsbok, the retinas of both eyes gleaming as she stood looking straight towards us – sharply alert and braced for trouble. Her head, with its pair of long javelin-like horns was held low – she was ready to charge at the drop of a hat, particularly an importunate veterinarian's hat! A movement of the torch to one side, and I glimpsed a small form even now rising unsteadily to its feet beneath its mother's belly. It was the calf – and in the wan shaft of light I could see what the Pakistani curator had described. A dark, serpentine body, some twelve inches long, was hanging from the left-hand side of its muzzle.

The gemsbok is a handsome antelope, native to the seasonally arid areas of southwest Africa. It has a short grey-fawn coat, white underparts and black and white markings on the head. The straight pointed horns, about three and a half feet long, are deadly lances that can impale a lion or a human with one fast swing of the powerful neck muscles. I had been the subject of one or two near misses from gemsbok horns and had seen them pierce two-inch-thick wooden planks at the toss of a head.

While the curator held his torch over my bag I rummaged in the contents preparing a flying syringe which I filled with Immobilon and loaded into my dart gun. I gave the syringe filled with the blue Revivon antidote to my companion. 'If anything goes wrong and I inject myself or collapse, stick this into my buttocks,' I instructed. He gawped at me in the reflected light of his torch, but said nothing. He'd seen me work with this potent anaesthetic before and understood that what the American vets call the 'buddy' system was a sound precaution. Always have someone close by carrying the antidote. Vets had sometimes died through accidentally injecting themselves with minute quantities of Immobilon. Some years later a timely shot of Revivon was to save Chris Thurley when he was using the drug on elephants at a zoo in Kent, just as had happened to me while blowpiping an Immobilon-filled dart into a sealion in the early days of its use in zoo animals.

Taking the torch and holding it alongside the barrel of the dart gun, I aimed down its beam at the mother gemsbok standing some twenty yards away. No chance of a preferred side shot into the rump or side of the shoulder with the animal steadfastly maintaining a head-on position towards the torch no matter how I moved it. With the gemsbok making a difficult target for an injection into a suitable area of muscle, I lowered the gun and changed the needle on the flying syringe for one that was short and barbed. It would not penetrate so deep, but would inflict less damage if my aim was off target or the animal moved at the last moment. Immobilon acts effectively when given subcutaneously or into the fat beneath the skin, although it is somewhat slower to take effect. The barb would stop the short needle from rebounding out of the skin and being lost in the sand in the paddock. Spent syringes containing drops of Immobilon lying buried in sand are as dangerous as anti-personnel mines awaiting some unwary and bare foot to step on them at some time in the future. They are a constant worry of mine when working in hot countries. Finding a flying dart in soft sand is more difficult than the proverbial search for needles in haystacks, but it has to be seriously attempted when one goes astray. That's why I tend to use barbed needles so often. Naturally the barbs can only be used with anaesthetics where I am sure to be able to remove the needle after the drug has taken effect. But it is really only the anaesthetics that are potentially lethal threats to bare-footed human beings.

I took aim at the base of the gemsbok's neck and pulled the trigger. A sharp crack, and the flying syringe with its bright blue flight hit the mark. The animal jumped backwards a little way and then stamped a warning forefoot. It continued to stare fixedly towards the torch. I put my finger to my lips as a gesture to warn the curator to remain silent. As the Immobilon began to take effect, the gemsbok would pass through a phase of being hypersensitive to sound. I didn't want it lurching off drunkenly into the darkness and then breaking its neck against the fencing. After a space of about two minutes, the female gemsbok's eyes began to glaze, she made chewing movements with her mouth, salivating moderately, and gently sank to her knees. Her haunches collapsed in seeming slow motion. The calf stood bewildered by her flank. It was time to move in.

'Doctor, beware of the snake. It could be a *djinn*, a demon in disguise,' the curator whispered as I walked towards the recumbent animal. He followed hesitantly a little way behind. The gemsbok teetered nervously as I reached it, but was loath to leave its unconscious dam. I grabbed it around the neck. 'Come on, Faisal, hold it,' I said.

'But, doctor, what if the viper detaches, what if . . .?' he replied.

'Hold it! At the rear end!' I ordered. The curator steadied the wriggling calf and I trained the torch on its head.

The smooth, gently tapering object hanging down from the muzzle looked for all the world like a snake. It was dark brown in colour with a 'head' that was rather wedge-shaped and a little broader than the rest of the cylindrical 'body'. And it was indeed firmly attached to the calf's skin. I ran my fingers down it and then up again to test how firmly it was rooted in the flesh. 'Aah doctor – it is indeed not a snake. I sincerely thought that it was not,' said the curator with a giggle, his diagnosis changed in an instant. 'It is . . . a leech!'

It was neither leech nor snake, but a trichoma – a type of benign tumour composed of hair which in this instance was tightly compacted into a solid rope of tissue. I had seen one or two of them before but never so long nor in a newborn animal. During the calf's development within the uterus a few hair-making cells, for reasons we don't understand, started to function and multiply at a highly abnormal, breakneck speed, out of synchrony with all the other cells of the body which were steadily constructing the calf in an orderly manner. Apart from their excessive enthusiasm, the hair cells that did this were otherwise normal, and the growth they produced was not a cancerous malignancy. More complicated tumours, where cells of several types behave in this riotous way during foetal development can result in 'monster' babies – occurrences which in days gone by gave rise to lurid stories of 'dog-boys' and 'bird-boys' and, where they survived, to the sad spectacle of such individuals being put on public display as freaks.

In the case of this gemsbok calf, it needed nothing more

to be rid of the 'serpent' than an injection of local anaesthetic at the base of the tumour, a little dissection with a scalpel and a couple of stitches. A shot of Revivon into the sleeping mother's jugular vein, and after two minutes she abruptly returned to consciousness and stood up. Sniffing her offspring to check that all was well, she turned again to face us, eyes full of suspicion. By then, the curator and I were back on the other side of the fence. One doesn't hang around after giving the intravenous antidote.

Walking with me back to my car the curator carried the trichoma lying across the upturned palms of his hand. His air was one of reverence akin to that of a courtier bearing a crown on a cushion. 'May I keep it, doctor?' he asked.

'Of course.' I heard later that he sold it for two thousand dirhams to a third-rank sheikh as the mummified corpse of a snake which had wormed its way into the womb of a pregnant antelope. Friends and retainers of the sheikh were unanimous in their opinion that portions of the snake prepared in some suitable way for his consumption would do wonders for His Excellency's rumoured impotence.

I wondered whether the sheikh would have been interested in purchasing the five-legged Friesian calf which I delivered when I was a newly qualified vet working in my home town of Rochdale, or the eagle at Salzburg Zoo that had a perfect full-sized third set of talons growing out of its chest, or the tooth that I once removed surgically from the centre of a zebra's testicle tumour in Singapore.

Only once have I come across Siamese twins among my exotic animal patients. Called to assist a Przewalski's horse in difficulties giving birth at Belle Vue Zoo, I found the mare in the stable lying on her side in deep straw, with Matt Kelly, the greatly experienced head keeper, standing over her. The Irishman had stripped to the waist and both his arms were dripping with blood-streaked soapy water. 'Oi thought you'd never arrive,' he said, gritting his teeth audibly. 'Marge here's in big difficulties – been pushin' all night I've no doubt.' He waved a hand at her rear end. 'Oi've had a good feel – foal's there all right but oi can't make head nor tail of it.'

'In a terrible state of chassus,' I said.

'Don't ye mock the greatest Irish playwright that ever lived, me boyo,' he replied. 'Get yet jacket off and tell me how ye propose to get the foal out.'

Normally Przewalski's horse, the wild species that is the ancestor of domestic horses and ponies and which probably became extinct in its last native haunts in Mongolia at the end of the 1960s, has to be approached warily, for it is a tough biter and kicker if roused. But on this occasion, with a difficult labour in progress, the mare allowed me to examine her, take her pulse under the lower jaw, press a fist into her belly and finally, after scrubbing up and then lubricating my arm with a shower of Lux soap flakes, to feel inside the vagina. I didn't need to tranquillize her as I knelt close to her hind legs. Most wild animals I'd had to assist in labour called a temporary truce between beast and man. I knew the mare would realize without understanding that I was there to help not to harass, though some of the things I had to do would be uncomfortable, perhaps even painful, and that the pain was unavoidable and not wilfully, clumsily or carelessly inflicted, as is so often unfortunately the case when humans are involved with animals. Dangerous creatures like giraffe, zebra and Cape buffalo, which would at other times have kicked, lunged or bitten if approached too closely, let alone touched on the rear quarters, had let me put my hand and arm deep into the birth canal while they stood or lay patiently waiting for the magical, mysterious process of conception, pregnancy and birth to be finally completed. Once the baby, the foal, calf, cub or pup was out and breathing air for the first time, the truce ended – except in those memorable cases, always in apes or monkeys, where a mother would let me take, or even hand me, her baby, not just immediately after its birth, but whenever I went to see them in the days that followed. That's the sort of thing that makes me continually glad that I chose to be a *wild* animal vet and not a horse or dog doctor, let alone a physician to human beings. With animals other than primates, however, as soon as the labour-truce ends, business returns to normal. I don't blame the animals – but those rare moments or occasionally hours when I can be truly intimate with a wild creature at the time of giving birth to new life without the use of drugs to dope and deaden its awareness of my presence, are very precious.

Kneeling in the straw, I slid my arm deeper into the Przewalski's mare, feeling my fingers pass through a fully relaxed, wide-open cervix and coming to rest on what felt like a panful of parboiled leeks. They were the feet and lower parts of the limbs of the foal. Now to establish by touch alone how the foetus was lying, and then decide how best to help its delivery. I began by identifying the legs – sorting out fore legs from hind legs – and I quickly discovered that I had a total of five limbs! 'It's twins, Matt,' I said as I withdrew for more soap flakes. 'That's where the trouble lies – both trying to come through the one door at the same time. I'll push one of them back and bring out the other first.'

Inside the mare again I soon found two hind legs that were obviously joined to the same trunk. Preferring to deliver a foetus backwards, because of the certainty that the head and neck will be self-straightening as the trunk moves through the pelvic girdle, I inserted my other arm so that I must have looked to Matt as if I was diving into the animal's vagina, and while pulling gently on the two joined hind legs with my right hand, blocked the other three limbs from following with my left. There was a little movement. To bring the foal's own pelvis through that of its mother, I tilted it by pulling on only one of the two legs I had grasped. The mare groaned. I strained to draw the leg towards me, hampered by the lack of space due to the presence of my other arm. Nothing budged. I was sweating when I withdrew and went to my bag for calving ropes. With these looped round the hind legs, Matt could pull upon one or the other as I instructed and I would need to have only my right arm inside the mare. It didn't work out like that. No matter how hard I tried, exerting pressure on first one of the foal's legs and then the other, I could not get it to move. I tried to bring the other foal out after finding its head and fore legs and repelling his twin by laboriously folding the obstinate hind legs back into the uterus and pushing his rump towards the mare's head. When half an hour had passed, my hands becoming cramped with increasing frequency, I gave up. 'It's got to be a Caesarian,' I said to the head keeper. 'No other way.'

Matt grimaced, his square, handsome face full of concern for his Marge. He scratched his shiny pate strewn with its thin covering of silvery hairs like rushes on a marble floor. 'Are ye sure ye just don't need that extra pound of pull?' he asked. 'Shall Oi try me hand?'

'No, no, it's not a matter of brute force – the foals both seem quite small. Something else is holding them back and I can't work out what it is.'

'Do ye think she'll survive a Caesar?'

'Can't see why not. I did one a month ago at Flamingo Park on a zebra.' It had been the first Caesarian section ever done on a zebra and in those days the operation was still an uncommon one on any kind of equine, including the domestic horse, with a fairly high risk of complications such as post-operative peritonitis.

Matt clicked his teeth noisily. 'Let's get crackin' then,' he said. 'What will ye be needin'?'

It took a little time to assemble everything I required for the operation. No fancy hospital here with a theatre for surgery like Regent's Park or San Diego Zoo. I would operate, as so often I do still, in the animal's own quarters without benefit of sterile surroundings, sophisticated electronic monitoring equipment or fancy gas machines. I always carry a sterile pack of basic surgical instruments, swabs and drapes in my car. While Matt fetched more warm water and extra heaters for the stable, I gave the mare a pre-med injection of xylazine as a sedative prior to full anaesthesia by intravenous barbiturate. Corticosteroids for shock and antibiotics to guard against later infection were the next items of importance.

When everything was ready and the now anaesthetized mare was breathing steadily with a strong regular heart beat, I began the operation, cutting quickly in through her flank and wasting as little time as possible by clamping only the bigger blood vessels, so vital was it to work fast if we were going to be successful. When the blue-white uterine wall lay shining like raw cuttlefish at the base of the incision, I pressed it and felt the bone of the skull within. I cut once more and there into my hands emerged the slippery brown head of a Przewalski's foal, its eyelids closed as if in contented slumber. Matt grunted as he helped lift the foal out of the uterus. Then he gasped in surprise.

'Blessed Mother, look at that!' he exclaimed as we stared at the cause of the difficult birth. The foal was almost completely out of the uterus – only its right foreleg remained to come clear, but that foreleg did not belong to it alone. It was shared by its twin – the one leg formed the right foreleg of one foal and the left foreleg of the other. 'Soi-amese twins!' whispered Matt in awe. 'Soi-amese twins by all that's Holy!' It took both of us all our strength to bring the joined twins away from the mare's body. While I injected a hormone to shrink the uterine wall and then began suturing the various layers of tissue with cat gut and finally, braided nylon for the skin, Matt fussed over the foals. 'They're aloive, both are males!' he cried as he cleared mucus and strands of membrane from their nostrils where they lay in the straw behind me.

I glanced round. They were indeed breathing and blinking their eyes. 'Rub them hard with a twist of straw and the towel,' I said. 'Dry them off and then give them a shot of picrotoxin – it's in my bag.' The respiratory stimulant would help to counteract the effect of any barbiturate they'd absorbed from their mother.

By the time I finished sewing up the mare, Matt had lifted the foals so that they stood on their feet – all seven of them. The shared leg was actually a fusion of two limbs. Each had about three quarters of its own shoulder blade, but from the shoulder-joint downwards there was but a single double-thickness humerus, radius, ulna and set of foot bones tipped with one tiny glistening yellow hoof. When they attempted to walk they at once collapsed in a heap. I examined them thoroughly but could see no way of separating them by surgery. 'They'll not be able to suckle,' said Matt sadly, after he had watched the pair in silence for a long time. Marge was raising her head, beginning to come round from the anaesthetic. 'Oi doubt they're able to get to their feet without help.'

He was right as it turned out. The twins proved unable to coordinate their movements in order to rise from the ground, take a few steps, or lie down. They struggled against one another until they lost heart and became fatigued. Typically the Irish head keeper worked hard to help them. He moved them to his room in the elephant house and stayed with them day and night, feeding them from a bottle and trying to teach them to cooperate in using the shared leg. They lived for four days and then the one that Matt had named Paddy developed severe enteritis and quickly died. I considered separating the survivor, Flynn, from his dead brother to see if he could use the leg when it was his alone. But in the end I decided there were too many risks and I didn't feel justified in subjecting the young foal to speculative, complicated surgery under the circumstances. I euthanased Flynn with an overdose of barbiturate while Matt, eyes glistening, cradled him in his arms.

9
Death of a Prairie Dog

All ceremonial due to them was taken away, they were
launched ten in one heap, twenty in another, the gallant and
the beggar together, the husband saw his wife and his deadly
enemy whom he hated within a pair of sheets . . .

Thomas Dekker, Elizabethan dramatist, on the mass
graves in London during the Plague of 1603

During the reign of King Henry VIII an edict was
promulgated with the object of controlling the plague. 'Set
the sign of the cross on every house affected for forty days
. . . no sick person to go abroad for one month . . . kill dogs
other than hounds, spaniels or mastiffs and confine those.'

Outbreaks of the plague or Black Death have been
recorded since time immemorial. The Bible tells of it smiting
the Philistines as punishment for stealing the Ark of the
Covenant. Gibbon suggested that the dread scourge killed
one hundred million people among three generations and in
all parts of the Roman Empire, and it may well have played
an important part in the fall of the latter. It arrived in
Britain at Weymouth in 1348, shortly after the English
victory at Crécy, and from then on one epidemic followed
steadily upon another, often annually in the late summer,
until the last major outbreak died out in 1667.

'Ring a ring o' roses, a pocket full of posies. A-tishoo!
A-tishoo! All fall down.' The familiar children's rhyme
originated on the continent where folk danced in the streets,
crying to God for salvation from the pestilence, until they
collapsed from exhaustion. The ring o' roses refers to the
rash on the skin, a symptom of the plague. The pocket full
of posies were nosegays carried to disguise the smell of

putrefying corpses. All fall down, of course, was what inevitably happened to the sufferers.

It has been suggested that the legend of the Pied Piper of Hamelin, with its reference to large numbers of rats and the disappearance of children, may have its origin in a real-life epidemic of the plague in the German town of Hameln in medieval times.

Nowadays some monuments, gravestones, ancient chronicles and traditions, such as the well-dressing ceremonies in Derbyshire, are our only reminders of a monstrous disease that in just three years during the fourteenth century killed a quarter of the population in Europe and half of that in England and Italy.

Like me, you may well find medical history of this sort endlessly fascinating, and enjoy sitting over the after-dinner port contentedly theorizing upon the several ways in which the microscopic plague bacillus undeniably changed the political map and social development of Europe. But enough of this – I set out to tell you about a pretty little furry creature, actually half a dozen pretty little furry creatures, that I was looking at through the window of their splendid new indoor quarters in a German zoo.

'What do you think of them, *Herr Doktor*?' asked the curator. 'When they begin breeding it will be a fine sight to observe them in their interlinking underground burrows through the one-way glass with the red lighting.' Dark red lighting which didn't disturb the animals had become all the rage in the latest designs of small mammal houses. The animals were prairie dogs, small brown rodents, cheeky and inquisitive, of the squirrel family. For me, one of the most charming sights at the zoo in Madrid during warm weather is the prairie dogs, popping up out of their holes in the lawns and surveying their surroundings with bead-like eyes, ever on the lookout for titbits.

'Where did you acquire them?' I asked.

'From a sailor up in Hamburg. He brought them back from the States as pets for his children. But they found them less amenable to handling than hamsters or gerbils, and gave them to us. We've got them in quarantine, just in case.'

'Illegal imports, stuffed in a matelot's kitbag, don't you think?'

'Very possibly. But of course he says they came in with all the proper papers.'

'Did you ask for the documents?'

'Naturally. He said the *Zoll*, the customs people, retained them. We're making inquiries.'

The prairie dogs were not the reason for my visit to the zoo. A wallaby had developed a suspicious lump on its jawbone and the curator had called me in to check whether or not the cause was the potentially fatal disease actinomycosis, commonly called 'Lumpy Jaw', so frequently seen in these creatures. The prairie dogs were simply something the curator wanted to show me as we walked around the zoo.

'They're doing well on the whole,' he said. 'One did die last night. No particular reason that we could see. But you know how fragile small mammals can be.'

'Did it show any signs of illness before popping its clogs?' I asked.

'Not a lot. Listless for a few hours, that was all. The body is in the refrigerator. Would you like to autopsy it, *Herr Doktor?*'

In my opinion, Germany is one of the easiest places for a zoo vet to work in Europe, and here, as in most German zoos, there was a well-equipped laboratory with every facility for autopsies. Why not, I thought, I'd never post-mortemed a prairie dog before. 'Let's do it,' I said. 'But it's probably nothing more than a sudden inflammation of the guts. Small mammals of this kind die at the drop of a hat, and prairie dogs' life expectancy is a maximum of two and a half years.'

We went to the laboratory and while I put on disposable plastic gloves, the curator fetched the small corpse from the refrigerator. With scalpel and scissors I unzipped the chill remains of the prairie dog. There wasn't much to see out of the ordinary, except that the spleen appeared to be very enlarged. But nothing ever dies for no reason. No heart simply stops. No creature, not even an ant, merely gives up the ghost. 'Get me some swabs,' I said to the curator. 'I'll take samples of heart blood and this big spleen.' An ever-so-dim glimmer of light was flickering somewhere in the farthest reaches of my mind. The curator handed me the bacteriological swabs – blobs of sterile cotton wool on the end of thin wooden sticks. I pressed the bud of one swab into an incision I'd made in the heart wall and used another in a similar manner on the spleen. The swabs I then placed in sterile plastic tubes containing a nutrient medium that would feed any bacteria which were present and keep them alive and contented until the laboratory could get to work on them.

'What do you think?' asked the curator, as I washed my hands.

'Almost certainly septicaemia, blood poisoning, caused by any one of several species of bacteria.'

It might well be Pasteurella. That faint light flickered again, and at once was gone. The Pasteurella family of germs is a common cause of serious disease in animals, both domesticated and wild. *Pasteurella haemolytica* is sometimes responsible for rapidly developing fevers in cattle being transported – so called 'shipping fever'. The chlorinated water of an open-air pool in Switzerland couldn't sterilize quickly enough some bird droppings that fell into it carrying the same species of bugs, before it somehow, perhaps via mouth, eye or blow-hole, entered the body of a one-year-old dolphin that I had watched being born. Within hours the dolphin was dead from septicaemia. Another kind of Pasteurella, *Pasteurella pseudotuberculosis*, can suddenly kill individual birds or mammals of almost any kind. Rarely do we have time to diagnose the disease in the living animal, and the germ is also very resistant to antibiotics. In zoos sporadic deaths in anything from exotic birds to wallabies to monkeys are frequently due to this bacterium, brought in by the ubiquitous scavenging pigeons and sparrows.

Only the laboratory could confirm whether or not Pasteurella had also ended the life of the little prairie dog, but in my experience it was the best bet to be the villain of the piece. The swabs were sent off to the bacteriology laboratory at the Veterinary Institute and my thoughts turned to other things.

My next port of call was Zurich, to give evidence at a court hearing. The case was a civil one between two Swiss men, each of whom claimed ownership of a particular dolphin. My involvement was concerned with how easy, or otherwise, it was to identify visually such an animal, how long distinctive scars might take to fade, taking into account their remarkable and rapid powers of healing, and so forth. I decided to travel by train from Germany and caught the Rheingold Express, long a favourite of mine, because of its route which for much of the way runs along one bank of the Rhine. I sat by a left-hand window in the restaurant car with my matjes herring and cold beer and watched as the Lorelei rock, the Mausturm, where Archbishop Hatto of Mainz, so legend has it, was eaten to death by mice in AD 970, and the steep vineyards of Bingen and Rudesheim, glided by. In the old gold haze of the late summer afternoon the mighty river and its castles, its barges and its drowsy little towns had never looked so beguiling. I sipped my Dortmunder and forgot about the little dead prairie dog.

Twenty-four hours later the prairie dog was suddenly anything but forgotten. I was in the airport at Zurich waiting for my flight to London when I heard my name called over the tannoy system. 'Will Dr Taylor of the International Zoo Veterinary Group go at once to the medical unit.' The message was repeated three times. There was no doubt it referred to me. But 'Medical Unit'? What on earth did that mean? It wasn't as if I were an illegal immigrant from some yellow fever area without vaccination papers and on the loose. I made inquiries, found the Medical Unit and went into an office plastered with malaria, typhoid and hepatitis posters.

'Dr Taylor? There is a most urgent phone call for you from Germany.' The white-coated blonde secretary pressed a button on her telephone and handed me the receiver.

'Hallo! Is that you, *Herr Doktor?*' It was the voice of the curator from the zoo that I had visited on the previous day. 'Thank goodness I got hold of you. Your home told me you should be at the airport at this time.'

'What's the matter?' I asked beginning to feel tense and uneasy.

'It's the swabs we sent to the lab. From the prairie dog. Colonies of bacteria have grown in just twenty-four hours. Pasteurella!'

I relaxed a little, but still wondered why he had felt it necessary to communicate the lab results to me with such urgency. I would be at home in England in about two and a half hours' time. 'As I suspected,' I said. 'Pasteurella. Sudden death from a Pasteurella septicaemia. It's a common thing in rodents.'

'No, *Herr Doktor*, no. It isn't *Pasteurella haemolytica*, the sort we usually have seen. It's something far worse. Another Pasteurella.' The curator sounded almost frantic. The light that had flickered in my mind when I had seen the enlarged spleen at the post-mortem blazed, dazzled, even as he started to speak again. '*Herr Doktor* – the lab says its *Pasteurella pestis*. You know it?'

I knew it all right, though I'd never met it before. *Pasteurella pestis* was the cause of plague, bubonic plague. He was talking about the Black Death.

There is a chillingly vivid passage in a fourteenth-century document that refers to the Black Death. 'Death came driving after, and all to dust dashed Kings and Knights, Kaisers and Popes, learned and lewd, he let no man stand even, that ever stirred after. Many a lovely lady, and

lemans* of Knights, swooned and swelted for sorrow of
Death's dints.'

The same germ that decimated the population of all parts
of Europe between the fifteenth and seventeenth centuries is
still around, though human epidemics are, thankfully, rare.
Transmitted generally by fleas (in the Great Plague of
London rat fleas were the culprits), the disease bacteria live
permanently among rodents of which there are over two
hundred species. It is always *somewhere* in the large
populations of such rodents as ground squirrels – and
prairie dogs – in areas of the New World like the American
West. Over forty people have died of the plague in the USA
since 1900. One was a vet who treated an infected ground
squirrel in 1977. The good news is that the disease, if
diagnosed and tackled promptly, is susceptible to certain
antibiotics. Where our medieval ancestors could but put
their faith in masses, invocations, nosegays and desperate
dancing to avert the pestilence, nowadays there are Terram-
cyin and effective flea-killing chemicals.

'Please telephone the Veterinary Institute,' said the
German curator. 'They urgently want to talk to you.'

I didn't waste a moment's time discussing the surprising
turn of events, but at once put a call through to the
Institute. Definitely the plague bacillus, they told me. The
state veterinary service was now, naturally, involved. The
remaining prairie dogs in the zoo quarantine, though still
apparently looking healthy, would be euthanased, rather
than given antibiotics. I regretted that decision, but could
not argue. Their quarters were being fumigated. The sailor
and his family had been traced and were already at an
infectious disease clinic being checked for signs of plague.
Their home would be fumigated, and their two pet cats
given a stiff course of tetracycline and thoroughly dusted
with Alugan flea powder. Legal proceedings against the
sailor would undoubtedly follow.

* leman – lover or sweetheart

'That leaves you, *Herr Doktor*,' said the bacteriologist who had outlined the measures being taken. 'You did the autopsy. You'd better take maximum precautions!'

After he rang off, I felt mildly shocked. The plague. I had done the autopsy using gloves and had afterwards scrubbed thoroughly with soap and disinfectant. There had been no signs of any fleas in the coat of the dead prairie dog, but . . . Normally I have some tetracycline tablets in my black bag – on this occasion I hadn't. The airport Medical Unit was the best place to obtain some without waiting until I got home, however, and to take other sensible precautionary measures. A supply of the antibiotics was given to me at once when I explained what had occurred to the medical officer on duty, and I swallowed the first tablet immediately. Then I was taken into a washroom where I stripped off and showered using mercury soap. After towelling dry, the doctor fumigated me, along with my clothing and black bag. I missed my plane of course, and while I sat waiting for the next, with the faint whiff of fumigant still clinging to me, my thoughts returned again and again to the ancient disease that I had met in, for me, such mundane circumstances.

There were no further outbreaks of the disease in animals or humans in Germany in the days that followed, and I continued in rude health. When I told Andrew all about my brush with *Pasteurella pestis* he said, 'Maybe we should provide you with Cardinal Wolsey's protection against the plague, when you go gadding about the continent from now on.'

'What was that?'

'An orange, filled with a sponge soaked in vinegar. He carried it with him everywhere.'

'I'll remember that next time I'm asked to autopsy a prairie dog.'

10
Christmas in the Camargue

The vilest of beasts is the belly.

Greek proverb

At Christmas 1992 we went down to the sea marshes of the Camargue. Years ago, while on the jury of a natural history film festival, I had discovered the Mas du Clarousset set amongst the pampas of tall reeds and the mud flats that are the haunts of flamingos and egrets, black bulls and white horses. Possessing an extraordinarily fine kitchen, even for Provence, it seemed the ideal place to spend the festival, with the high point being my intention to ride on horseback across the swampland to Midnight Mass in the tall fortress church of Les Saintes Maries de la Mer. It was on this latter romantic pilgrimage that things went wrong.

The night was moonless, and my cream-coloured Camarguais horse, unpropitiously named Mouton (sheep), got lost in the wastes of black mud under a black sky, and I found myself alone, far behind the other riders. Mouton ground to a halt in the pitch darkness and I could not persuade her to proceed in any direction whatsoever. Feeling uncomfortably like the Knight of the Woeful Countenance halted on his way to the Most Solemn Celebrations of Our Lord's Birth, I waited to be rescued and wondered what on earth Salinger was thinking about when he had someone in *The Catcher in the Rye* say: 'I'd rather have a goddam horse. A horse is at least human, for God's sake.' A local *gardien* eventually located Mouton and me and with much whooping and yee-hawing, at last got my ovine equine to start off again and then to trot on quickly, blindly, through the mire in order to make up time. My mutton-headed steed promptly stumbled, I fell off into the ooze, and thus we arrived at the church caked with mud long after Mass had begun and with the congregation overflowing into the village square. I spent the next hour ruefully nursing my bruises and drinking Côtes du Rhône in a nearby bar with gypsy guitars instead of the Gloria in Excelsis as accompaniment.

I've always had a healthy respect for horses, though I consider them relatively stupid animals. What I was told as a student – that if you can handle a horse you can handle any creature – seems broadly true to me, and since beginning to work purely with exotic animals I have never been hurt or injured to anything like the same degree that I was in my early days of general practice with horses. Domestic horses have kicked me, bitten me, stamped on me and rolled on me during examinations and treatment. Only a horse has ever resulted in me having to be pushed to an aircraft in a wheelchair. Only a horse has made me vomit with the pain of an iron-shod blow to my thigh.

In over thirty years of exotic practice I've been lucky, or perhaps it's because of the precautions, sometimes involving tranquillizers, that we take when working hands-on with wild creatures. I've suffered nothing more serious than a leopard claw hooked into an Achilles tendon, a monkey bite to the bone of one finger, assorted bruises by elephants and hippopotamuses and bites from two venomous snakes, one of which had been devenomed surgically, the other, an English adder, not penetrating deeply enough, and one constrictor snake which, while painful, contained no poison. My sudden, undignified, nocturnal descent from Mouton brought back memories of the days of my youth. Thank goodness, I often think, for the tranquillity of my *wild* animals. Not for me the fractious horse – or the hard-biting, owner-adoring, vet-hating corgi or the fireball, domestic tom cat that has somehow to be hauled out from its hidey hole behind the chamber pot under some doting old lady's bed. Those are *wild animals*, man!

It was my kind of horse, a wild horse called a kulan, that occupied my attention for some weeks, two years before, during the winter of 1990. Kulans are biscuit-coloured Asiatic wild asses with short-cropped black manes that are now confined in the wild to reserves in Turkmenistan, but are thriving and breeding well in many zoos around the world. The individual in question lives in a Spanish zoo and when I was asked to examine it had slowly been losing weight for almost six months. Otherwise its behaviour was apparently normal and its appetite for hay, pony cubes, apples and carrots undiminished.

'It's a mystery to me,' said the resident vet. 'Nothing to see, no symptoms, just getting thinner, *poco a poco*. I'm beginning to fear the worst.' His face was troubled. I knew what he was fearing, particularly in this zoological garden. Tuberculosis. Over the years we had battled against TB in many species in the collection, particularly the primates, and had had some success in bringing it under control among them by a combination of tuberculin tests applied to the apes' and monkeys' eyelids, and prophylactic dosing with isoniazid and pyrazinamide. Tuberculin testing in many other kinds of animals such as the big cats doesn't work, and can be very unreliable in exotic hoofed stock. Blood tests for the disease were being developed in some medical laboratories, but such facilities were hard to come by in Spain.

The old scourge of tuberculosis, consumption as it was called in days gone by, is beginning to rear its head again. Even with improved sanitation, modern methods of meat and milk inspection and well-tried systems of skin testing and vaccination, the disease was never, unlike smallpox, eradicated. Now it is making a comeback in the human population and perhaps also among animals.

In my field we've had many successful cures of tuberculous animals using special antibiotics like rifampicin administered in lengthy courses, but now the tough, waxy bacterium that is the cause of the disease is becoming resistant to rifampicin and many, many other anti-TB drugs. If not yet truly on the march again, tuberculosis is certainly gathering its forces and making forays.

The occasional animal in a zoo in Spain and elsewhere – an oryx, gazelle or lion, perhaps – that simply wastes slowly away, becomes 'consumptive' as its body is seemingly 'consumed', frequently turns out at post-mortem to be a case of tuberculosis. The kulan, all its ribs plainly visible through the skin, seemed likely to be just such a one.

I watched it walking around its paddock, its breath steaming in the cold air. Nothing unusual in its gait. It stood still. 'Did you see that?' I said. 'When it stopped walking?' The kulan had momentarily flicked up a hind leg and lightly tapped it against its belly. It began walking again, and when it came once more to a halt, repeated the curious half-hearted kick. 'It's got some discomfort in its belly,' I said. 'But it doesn't strike me quite like the behaviour of a horse with a colic.'

The vet nodded. 'I haven't noticed that before,' he replied. 'But I agree, it isn't the kick of a colicky animal.'

'Let's knock it out with xylazine,' I said. 'Take some blood and I'll try to get a TB test done in England.' It didn't take long to dart and sedate the kulan, leaving it standing but oblivious to my slipping a sample needle into its jugular. I examined the animal but found nothing of note.

A week later the laboratory reported on the kulan blood sample. They couldn't guarantee it – kulans were something new to them, was it a kind of South American monkey? – but they were pretty certain it was negative for TB. Other tests showed the animal was slightly anaemic, but otherwise its organs were functioning normally. When I went back to Spain I watched the kulan again. The odd little kick at the belly was still occurring. Nothing very dramatic. Blink your eyes and you'd miss it.

'We must do *something*,' said the Spanish vet. 'If it's not

TB, do you think it might be a tumour?' It was certainly a strong possibility – a growth, benign or malignant, perhaps in the chest cavity, more likely in the abdomen. No X-ray machine, at least none in Spain, was powerful enough to penetrate the kulan's bulk. There was only one thing to be done: I decided on an exploratory laparotomy – open up the kulan's belly and have a look around at its insides.

After keeping the kulan off food for twenty-four hours and water for twelve, I anaesthetized it with Immobilon, ideal for this type of creature, though it does tend to push up the blood pressure. Keepers supported the kulan so that it lay on its back, all four legs in the air, while I opened the abdomen precisely along the midline beginning just behind the breastbone. Then it was a matter of rooting about in the kulan's *callos* (tripes), as my colleague called them, using a combination of sight and touch. There were no tumours, but before long I came along an angry red area on the outside of the stomach about the size of a small saucer. After prodding it I came to the conclusion that it was the base of a large ulcer – about fifteen times bigger than the sort favoured by overworked middle-class businessmen.

An incision into the stomach confirmed that it was indeed a chronic gastric ulcer, the first I'd ever seen in any equine. Surgical removal of gastric ulcers in animals is rarely done, especially since the advent of modern anti-ulcer drugs, but this case demanded it, I felt. I cut out an elliptical area of stomach wall containing the circular ulcer and then began closing the hole with sutures placed in such a way that its edges were slightly folded inwards. Two layers of sutures gave extra security against the highly undesirable possibility of a post-operative leak of stomach fluids. My colleague completed the operation by closing the peritoneum, abdominal muscles and skin with strong nylon thread. We injected antibiotics and cortisone, and finally reversed the Immobilon anaesthetic with an intravenous shot of Revivon. Five minutes later the kulan was on its feet and looking around for food. 'Give it a little warm water to drink in an hour,' I said. 'But no food until tomorrow, and then only a little from time to time.'

The kulan didn't kick at its belly any more, and over the next few weeks made a full recovery. Weight was slowly regained, and when I saw it some four months later it was in fact rather on the plump side.

Gastric ulcers similar to those of human beings are uncommon in most species of animal. The majority of my cases have been in dolphins, sealions, giraffes and giant pandas. A variety of often vague symptoms may be presented by a patient, and nowadays we reach at once for our flexible endoscope in order to take a look inside the stomach. With dolphins no anaesthetic or sedative is necessary to do this, but other animals require at least some degree of tranquillization. Our 1.6 metre endoscope is one of the longest manufactured but it can still only go as far as the stomach of a young giraffe.

Treatment of gastric ulcers by medical, rather than surgical means, posed problems for me in the old days. Then, humans with typical gastric (peptic) ulcers would be put on a bland diet, warned particularly to avoid eating fatty fish such as mackerel, and prescribed antacids such as Maalox or Bismuth. My difficulty was that dolphins and sealions thrive best on mackerel and herring, and have no appetite for milk pudding, dried toast or poached plaice! Giraffes turn their noses up at Maalox. Only the giant pandas will cooperate with their physician and forgo hard bamboo cane for a while to lap up bowls full of boiled rice, milk, honey and Complan invalid food, all mixed together with a proprietary brand of stomach antacid. When the first of the modern anti-ulcer drugs for humans, Tagamet, was developed I began at once trying it out on my patients. The results were dramatic. Our endoscopy showed bleeding gastric ulcers healing completely within two or three weeks of the treatment commencing. A male giant panda arrived in Madrid from China with a large, ugly, active ulcer. Tagamet tablets soon sorted that out.

Most dolphins or sealions, whose ulcers may be related to their high intake of mackerel, fish which can contain much histamine, a chemical thought to play a significant part in the creation of ulcers, gulp down their tablets hidden inside the gills of a fish. There are a few wily old lags who chew a fish very carefully specifically to find and spit out such hidden objects. We try to outwit them by first throwing them half a dozen 'undoctored' succulent fresh herring when they are hungry. They chew them and, finding them to be kosher, greedily open their mouth for more, all suspicions lulled. The tablet goes in fish number seven which, hopefully, they swallow whole.

Other excellent drugs, Zantac and Losec, came on the market after Tagamet and we use them effectively on patients that have ranged from elephant to killer whale. Kora, a young elephant at Windsor Safari Park, certainly has an ulcer of her gullet and may have others in her stomach. We can't be sure because the endoscope isn't long enough. She has been under intensive treatment using Losec and other drugs by John, my partner, backed up by the exceptionally skilled and dedicated nursing of her keepers. She is weighed each day, the graph of her gains and losses providing an essential aid in monitoring her progress. With the dispersal of all the stock at Windsor soon to commence, finding a first-class placing for Kora and her companions as an established family is one of our top priorities. Wherever she goes we must be able to continue overseeing her treatment and veterinary and nursing facilities and personnel will have to be up to Windsor's level. I hope desperately that at least one of the Windsor elephant keepers will go to work at Kora's new home.

Dolphins sometimes show symptoms of tummy trouble like that we associate with ulcers, but for quite different reasons. This is particularly true of the ones I call the 'tidy' dolphins. They are individuals who love to hoover up and swallow autumn leaves that fall on the water surface, and meticulously gather objects that drop accidentally into their pools. Some of these houseproud dolphins take the nuts, bolts, pieces of plastic, coins, or whatever, that they find, and straight away give them to their trainer. Swallowed leaves are generally regurgitated naturally from time to time, and cause no trouble. Other dolphins, however, store leaves and assorted bric-à-brac in their first stomachs for long periods, sometimes filling themselves up to such an extent that there's no room for food fish. A 'loaded' dolphin in this condition is always hungry, but stops eating after the first few fish of a meal. A little while later it's hungry again. 'The Chinese Meal Syndrome' would be a good term for it. Obviously, if nothing is done about these 'dustbin' stomachs, the animals begin to lose weight and may well fall ill. In fact, it is quite simple and safe to wash the accumulated material out of a dolphin. We place it on a mat of plastic foam with two strong men holding its jaws open with looped wet towels, and then pass in a stomach tube. Several pints of warm water are stirrup-pumped in until, suddenly, 'whoosh', the water, together with its flotsam of leaves, plastic, nuts and bolts, gushes out of the mouth, soaking the vet of course, and all is well again. Until the next time. We wash out some dolphins regularly every autumn.

Some years ago a dolphin was sent from Israel to Switzerland. It was accompanied by a health certificate from a vet in Tel Aviv, but a week after arrival in its new pool it began to show signs of stomach trouble. The Swiss vet suspected a gastric ulcer and I was asked to go out with my endoscope and investigate. As soon as I looked down the instrument's eyepiece, after passing it down the dolphin's gullet, through the valve at the bottom, and into the stomach, I saw what was wrong. I was looking inside a bulging money bag. The stomach was stuffed with dozens and dozens of coins.

It's odd how people love to throw coins into pools of any

kind – *Three Coins in a Fountain*, wishing wells and all that. In zoos the crocodile pools yield the greatest harvest of such currency – most of it thrown at the poor animals 'to make them move' or 'to see if they're real', as culprits explain when tackled by the reptiles' keepers. Unlike dolphins, crocodiles don't swallow coins. Some zoo pools collect sufficient cash each year to pay for the keepers' Christmas party or to send a fat cheque to a charity.

While my stomach tube was swilling the coinage out of the dolphin in Switzerland, the Marinelands' director, who had been told of my discovery, put a phone call through to Tel Aviv. An acrimonious conversation ensued. The dolphin wasn't as healthy as the Israeli certificate had indicated and, more to the point, who was going to pay for bringing me over from England to sort it all out? The Israeli defence was that the dolphin wasn't known to be 'tidy' and, as it had been in Switzerland for a week and was performing during the height of the summer season when there were many visitors, a significant proportion of whom were perhaps coin throwers, the money might well have been collected there. Not very plausible, but . . .

I entered the director's office carrying my haul of coins in a plastic bucket while the argument was still in full spate. 'I say again,' he was growling testily. 'There is no question but that you should be responsible for Dr Taylor's fee.' I could tell from the sour expression on his face that his opposite number in Tel Aviv didn't feel inclined to contribute one penny.

'Excuse me, *Herr Direktor*,' I interrupted. 'Many of the coins are Israeli ones and not likely to have been thrown by Swiss visitors. Would it not be fair for me to sort and count the coins, and for the Israelis and Swiss to pay a proportion of my fee according to the number, *not* the value, of agorots and Swiss francs that I find?'

The director's face was instantly transformed. 'Why not!' he said, and proceeded to explain my proposal into the telephone. He nodded vigorously. Tel Aviv had accepted. I poured the coins on to his desk and began to sort through them. By the time I had finished there were separate piles made up of two hundred and five Israeli coins, forty-four Swiss coins (of various denominations in both cases), two German ten-pfennig pieces, an Irish penny and a brass button. 'So if the Israelis pay about five-sixths of my account,' I said, 'and you one-sixth, that would be equitable, don't you think?'

'*Ja! Ja!*' the director chuckled. 'And you, *Herr Doktor*, can keep the twenty pfennigs and the Irish penny for your future travels!'

'What about the button?' I asked.

11

'Open Wide, Please!'

Good God, how much reverence can you have for a Supreme
Being who finds it necessary to include such phenomena as
phlegm and tooth-decay in His Divine system of Creation?

Joseph Heller, *Catch 22*

A balmy, purple-skied, blossom-perfumed June evening at
the Manoir aux Quat' Saisons. The Krug Imperial before
dinner had struck a chord that heralded the advent of
unspoken pleasures. The Norfolk squab baked in a salt
crust and served with *pommes Maxine* and a sliver of *foie
gras* enchanted your partner who now gazes into your eyes
over a last glass of the Château d'Yquem that had so
perfectly accompanied the *feuilleté tiède de poire William
rôti au gingembre citron vert*. In a moment dark coffee for
both of you. Fingers touch across the table top. In the
background the Chopin *étude* which you requested is being
played at precisely the right unintrusive volume. A lingering
glance between you is the smoke before fire. It will be a full
moon as you drive the Lagonda down the Oxfordshire
lanes. The house, ever warmly welcoming, will be empty
when you arrive. You will be alone, to sit together perhaps
on the terrace overlooking the stream where the swans
drowse at the reed's edge. Tremulous images of love, of a
burgeoning passion . . . *vanish at once* as the dagger of pain
shoots down a molar at the back of your mouth! A terrible,
throbbing, jaw-burning toothache instantly dispels any
thought of romance, sex, lust – and all other things except
The Molar.

No, please believe me when I say that I am *not* sitting in
my boudoir in a froth of pink chiffon, Barbara Cartland

writing under a pseudonym. I am simply describing what most of us have at some time or other experienced – that toothache can take your mind off anything, even the imminent promise of romantic sex. And what is true about human beings applies also to wild animals – as we have recently realized.

Unlike humans, who seem to be able to procreate in the most adverse conditions, animals are easily put off. Male cheetahs won't do it if there isn't any competition around in the form of other suitors, or if they feel too exposed to public gaze when, for example, the grass or undergrowth is too short. Flamingos won't do it if there aren't enough of them gathered together in a fairly tight group – usually over nineteen individuals in number – or if the pink colour of their plumage isn't striking enough, perhaps as a result of an inadequate diet. Sometimes we persuade a mere handful of flamingos to reproduce by surrounding their territory with mirrors which create the illusion of them being part of a much bigger social group. Giant pandas won't do it just because the pair of them have been selected arbitrarily by the Chinese for presentation to a foreign zoo or a famous zoologist called Edward Heath. Female giant pandas are like female human beings – they won't mate with just any old male thrust upon them. No arranged marriages for them. In the wild a female panda sits in the fork of a tree looking down on a selection of males who have travelled for miles during the breeding season to win her favours. They show off and do battle with one another and then, at her leisure, she selects the most attractive suitor. Beauty and perhaps character as far as pandas are concerned are in the eye of the beholder. Only a panda has the eye for such matchmaking.

There are, of course, many more mundane reasons for lack of breeding in wild animals. Infectious diseases of the reproductive system, nutritional and hormonal causes and, still, cases where zoos keep together animals of the wrong sex. Since we, in particular my partner Andrew, started

sexing birds surgically by abdominal endoscopy – introducing a fine viewing instrument under anaesthetic through the
belly wall to view the sex organs and determine whether
they are ovaries or testes, the number of 'childless' pairs of
parrots, vultures, cranes, storks and the like has dropped
dramatically. Two males or two females of species where
both sexes look identical from the outside, at least to the
human eye, are most unlikely to have offspring! The sexing
of some animals, most reptiles and some mammals such as
young beavers, can be very difficult for the inexperienced.

But it is only in the past few years that we have begun to
realize how important dental health is to the general well-
being, including the reproductive capacity, of the animals in
our care. Obviously we have always recognized the
existence of periodontal disease, tooth root abscesses and
malformed or mal-positioned teeth as important medical or
surgical conditions that occur, not uncommonly, in everything from lions to lizards. For years I have treated mouth
infections, particularly in snakes where they can produce
long-lasting and sometimes fatal consequences, and used my
forceps to pull sensitive teeth out of the jaws of sealions or
wolves that had developed a painful gum boil or infected
root canal after fracturing teeth, generally through fighting.
Caries, holes in the teeth of the type that need filling in
humans, are not common in animals. I had filled a few with
the old-fashioned mercury amalgam using an army war
surplus foot-pedalled dental drill when I was a young vet,
but in general *surgical* intervention, dentistry for my
patients consisted of nothing more complicated than
extractions under anaesthetic.

In the late Eighties we began to investigate the dental
problems of exotic animals in depth, in collaboration with
our human dental colleague, Peter Kertesz. It quickly
transpired that there were many techniques being used in
human dentistry which could be transposed to animals with
positive beneficial results on the animal's general health. We
were not interested at all in cosmetic dentistry, as used, in

the USA particularly, on the pugs and poodles of the rich, or in the restorative dentistry that gives police dogs new fanged teeth of titanium steel. Our aim was to use advanced dentistry, both preventative and therapeutic, where necessary to enhance the general health of exotic animals. Even in humans, few people realize how long-lasting tooth disease can sometimes affect major organs, such as the kidney or bone marrow, giving rise to significant effects potentially more serious than mere toothache or bad breath.

Clearly a raging toothache in a tigress or a cow elephant doesn't incline the female to succumb with abandon to the amorous advances of her mate. I suspect they would readily subscribe to a remark of Evelyn Waugh in *Vile Bodies* – 'all this fuss about sleeping together. For physical pleasure I'd rather go to my dentist any day.' At such times the mere approach of the veterinary surgeon bearing a powerful analgesic can be fraught with danger for the well-meaning physician, although I must say that trying to persuade an elephant to swallow a quarter of a pound of aspirin is ever a thankless task.

What we began to find, however, was that animals could suffer from mild, probably intermittent, bouts of pain in a tooth without obvious signs such as tenderness when eating, excessive salivation or pawing at the mouth. This low-level dental discomfort was enough, though, to put the sufferer off the joys of sex. Some apparently infertile or celibate individuals were like the morose old lady who lived nearby in Pilling Street when I was a boy, and whose irascible nature my grandmother considered to be due to the fact that her false teeth, always bought 'off the peg' at Woolworth's, never fitted, thus causing constant irritation and ulceration of her gums. She was, Grandma said, 'a martyr to her dentures'. We began to find some 'martyrs' among our animal patients.

At first Peter Kertesz did the odd bit of dental surgery on exotic animals for us. External fixation of a deer's fractured jaw, a kangaroo needing drainage of a root canal, a gorilla with a tender molar that required filling. He and his dental assistant operated while we anaesthetized and watched over the physiological state of the animal. Results were very encouraging and we moved on to bigger species.

To do that meant that the dental instruments, the probes, angled mirrors and drill heads of the sort with which the dentist litters your mouth when you sit in his chair, while he asks questions about your holiday plans that you are utterly incapable of answering, would no longer be of any use. Elephants and rhinoceroses require tools of a quite different order of magnitude. Peter, therefore, designed, and had manufactured, giant drills, forceps, elevators and so forth. His power source at first was a Black and Decker machine of the sort brandished by do-it-yourself handymen. They were the modern versions of the masonry chisel and steel mallet that I had used so many years before when laboriously extracting my first elephant molar in Manchester.

Gradually it came to pass that Peter worked on exotic animals instead of Mayfair socialites each and every Friday, and whereas previously it would have taken me hours of blood, sweat and chiselling to extract a diseased tusk from an elephant, his techniques and armamentarium, the latter weighing around two hundred and fifty pounds even for a relatively simple procedure, could take out one cleanly in little more than twenty minutes. Veterinary dentistry had made a great leap forward and, most significantly for us, when nagging gnashers were no more, an animal's thoughts turned to romance. Sex reared its beautiful head again. Particularly pleasing to me was the fact that we were able to use Peter's skills not merely on high-value 'glamorous' species like clouded leopards and elephants, but also on the humbler representatives of British wildlife, such as badgers and foxes rescued and rehabilitated by the admirable Wildlife Hospital Trust at 'St Tiggiwinkles' near Aylesbury where we are visiting consultants.

At the beginning of 1993 John Kershaw phoned me from

Marineland Côte d'Azur near Antibes. Tanouk, a male killer whale, had broken one of his large conical front teeth. The pulp cavity was exposed and bleeding slightly. I advised him to swab the damaged area with weak formaldehyde solution to sterilize and seal the cavity. That would hold the position temporarily. Broken teeth of this sort are not uncommon occurrences in wild, or domestic animals and seldom lead to root infection. But the latter does occasionally follow. A tooth root abscess in an adult male killer whale would be a formidable problem, and might easily put at risk the life of an animal worth one million dollars or more. Just opening the huge and powerful mouth of such a creature, let alone anaesthetizing it for surgery, is fraught with difficulties and risks. I had had forcibly to open the mouths of killer whales many times in order to pass stomach tubes, and what a stressful, sometimes dangerous, business it had been. Several tons of killer whale thrashing about with a wooden gag the size of a railway sleeper between its jaws can be tricky to approach, let alone begin thrusting hands or instruments into its toothy maw.

I telephoned Peter Kertesz. 'I need a killer whale tooth filling in France,' I told him.

He'd never tackled one of these beasts before, and I could sense pleasurable anticipation mixed with a slight trace of apprehension when he replied. 'It will be under anaesthetic, I presume?'

'No, I daren't risk a general and it would be impossible to get him to accept a jab of local into the gums or a nerve block with his mouth open. But from what John Kershaw has described, the tooth is devitalized, the nerve running down the pulp cavity is dead. You should be able to do it without anaesthetic.'

'Err . . . how? Can you prop the jaws open as it lies at the bottom of the drained hospital pool?'

'No. I want to try doing it while it floats in the water.'

There was silence for a few moments. Then Peter said, doubt now distinctly evident in his tone of voice, 'I can't float in the water in swimming trunks or a wet suit filling a whale's tooth!' He must have thought I'd been at the sherry bottle with a vengeance.

'Oh, absolutely not, Peter,' I said. 'The idea is to call the whale over to the side of the pool, get him to open his mouth so you can work on the tooth for a couple of minutes, give him a reward of fish, let him close it and then repeat the sequence.'

'So it's going to be like saying: "Say 'Aaah', Whale!" Will he do that?'

'Yes. And John will start training him to extend the open-mouth period as far as possible. Tanouk is a greedy guts, only too happy to open up for a handful of herring.'

'He won't clamp his jaws on my hand, quick as a flash?'

'Certainly not. Trust me, John and his team know Tanouk like a brother. The whale will do anything for them. But when he says "take your hand out now" you must do it instantly, and then wait a few minutes for a repeat performance.'

He considered this for a little while – his professional work depends on him possessing two intact hands – and then said, 'I'll have to use ultra-fast setting materials, and I have a suggestion to make. If I send some drill bits out to John, he could accustom the whale to their contact with the tooth by twiddling them in the cavity on a regular basis before the big day.'

'Great idea!' I said, and we at once arranged a date, a Friday as usual, four weeks later at the beginning of February, for us to travel down to Antibes with his dental nurse, Samantha, and Christine, the new lady in my life. We'd need the two girls' baggage allowance for all the gear Peter would be bringing along. And also that was a good excuse for us going to enjoy a post-operative bouillabaisse at La Coquille in Cannes!

The last dental operation on which Peter and I had cooperated concerned an elephant at Gerry Cottle's Circus headquarters. One of its tusks needed cutting back. Under general anaesthetic Peter had removed the offending portion with a portable circular saw, bored out the root canal with a drill bit as thick as my finger and then tapped the interior and screwed in a hard nylon plug. Finally he had smoothed and rounded the new tip of the tusk with a sander. The finished result was perfect and the repair invisible to the casual observer. Tanouk's tooth promised to be a far more delicate matter. The drill bits were sent over to Antibes by courier and John began familiarizing the whale by teasing the small metal objects into the fractured but insensitive tooth. Twiddle, twiddle went John with one of his bits. After a minute or so, he withdrew it, patted the whale on its forehead or 'melon' while saying 'Good boy, Tanouk', and dropped some plump herring, mackerel or capelin, the favourite fish of the Marineland's killer whales, down his throat. Tanouk seemed to find this a most enjoyable game. Going to the dentist as a boy in Rochdale, where old Mr Fearn had assured me that local anaesthetics were best not used for he 'liked to know when he was close to a nerve', had never been anything like this. It's certainly true that most of my patients receive more careful and considered treatment than anything dished out to mere *homo sapiens* under Mr Major's benighted NHS. Tanouk's filling was likely to cost the Marineland something in the range of £2,500 all told. But as Roland de la Poype, the owner of the organization had once remarked, 'Nothing but the best is good enough for any animal in our care.' And he didn't just mean killer whales or king penguins. Rescued seagulls with broken wings have always received the same meticulous attention when called for, regardless of the cost.

We all flew to Nice on the Thursday evening so that we had the whole of Friday to deal with Tanouk. John met us at the airport. 'What sort of mood is Tanouk in?' I asked him as we drove along the coast road past the Baie des Anges. Some years before, the BBC had filmed here an episode of

'One by One', the series based on my earlier experiences – one that was also principally concerned with killer whales.

'Grumpy,' he replied. 'Crotchety, utterly cheesed off.'

'Why?'

'I've separated him off from the females ready for the dentistry tomorrow. One of them is on heat and he is not well pleased.'

Peter gave me a questioning look. 'I could do with a glass of the Marineland's excellent Calvados when we arrive,' I said cheerily.

'So could I,' said Peter with some emphasis.

'Will *you* be sticking your arm down the mouth?' whispered Christine into my ear.

'No,' I replied.

She breathed a faint sight of relief, and then the car turned into Avenue Mozart. We had arrived at the dentist's.

Early to bed, early to rise – so much wiser when operating to be well rested and fresh. Next morning at 8 o'clock we had coffee and brioches in the Marineland while John's staff gave all the marine mammals, including Tanouk, their regular daily ration of vitamins and minerals.

'Sorry there's no twenty-year-old copies of *Country Life* or *Tatler* in the waiting room,' said John. Peter laughed. 'And I hope the patient has brushed his teeth before sitting in the chair,' he replied. 'Halitosis is something we dentists never really come to terms with.'

'I think you will find,' said the animal curator, 'that a killer whale's teeth are cleaner and the smell from his mouth sweeter than in most of your human patients.'

It's true – I've never really smelled bad breath from any animal except domestic dogs and cats with pronounced tooth or gum disease – or terminal kidney failure.

Peter, John and I discussed a plan of action with Bruce, John's No. 1 and senior whale trainer. He had been doing most of the familiarization of Tanouk with the dental equipment.

'He's completely accustomed to me exploring the hole in the tooth,' Bruce explained. 'Absolutely no tenderness, but bad-smelling material comes out frequently. Tanouk is even happy with vibration in his mouth. He floats happily at the pool side with his jaws open while I revolve a dental bit inside the cavity using a small wood-worker's drill!'

Peter, as usual, had been meticulous in researching the detailed dental anatomy of the patient in question, and after visiting the whale room at the Natural History Museum had a clear idea of what the inside of Tanouk's tooth must look like. The way the tooth was rooted in the jawbone was quite different from that in humans, the pulp cavity being shaped rather like a broad cone with its peak at the tooth's point. The further down he drilled the bigger the bit he would need to use. He showed us some of the special large-animal bits he'd had made out of tungsten carbide; there was one with an abrasive head that resembled a silver lychee. Just looking at it sent shivers down my spine! I pictured Peter as an even more sadistic Olivier in *Marathon Man*.

'David, what chances are there of the killer whale reacting badly to the oil of cloves I'll be using to disinfect the cleaned-out root?' Peter asked.

I had no idea. Nor, I am sure, was there anyone in the world who could answer the question with total confidence. 'Impossible to say,' I answered. 'But I'd be surprised if it caused any trouble. Whales tend not to be very drug-sensitive.'

We went to the side of the isolation pool where Tanouk was beginning to shake off the drowsiness of the night; he's not a quick waker-up at the best of times. The big whale's blasts of warm breath created short-lived cockades of vapour in the sharp late-winter air. The bright sun glanced off the gleaming black arch of his body as he rolled on his side to peruse the strangers with one dark-brown and intelligent eye.

A platform had been set up by the side of the pool from which the dental team could work. Samantha, the dental assistant, began to unpack Peter's amazing assortment of equipment and lay it on nearby tables draped with sterile green cloths. It might have been the twentieth-century version of the Inquisition torturer's ritual display of his instruments before the eyes of the accused, but in fact these often grotesque tools formed a unique armoury that had brought relief to the mouths of wild animals all over Europe.

Television crews and photographers had begun to arrive; killer whale dentistry sounded like too good a news item to miss. Bruce persuaded Tanouk to open his mouth for Peter's first inspection. The hole was as big as a marrowfat pea.

'Should be straightforward,' said Peter. 'So long as we can keep the cavity dry when we begin filling.' He'd already decided how to cope with that. Just before the whale closed his mouth and dipped his head beneath the water after each two-minute period of holding it open, the cavity would be plugged, not with some state-of-the-art silicone gel, nylon bung or any other of the materials that dental surgeons delight in. No, he would pop in a lump of home handyman's Blu-Tack, the stuff you use for sticking together bits of this and that. The Blu-Tack could quickly be flicked out of the cavity when the mouth opened again.

'Good! Let's begin!' Peter put on his head lamp now all was ready and gave a whirr of his high-speed drill, its wicked thistle-head sparkling in the morning sunshine.

That was the moment when Tanouk, like any human patient who is free to choose his or her favourite dentist, decided that, painless as it had so far been, there was only one person he entrusted with his teeth – Bruce. These other folk, strangers apart from John, didn't give him the necessary ring of confidence. So when Peter moved in with his drill, Tanouk clammed up, shut his mouth firmly. Bruce asked Tanouk to say 'aaah'. He opened wide. Peter's hand descended. Tanouk squirted a disrespectful mouthful of water over him (rinsing the mouth before the drilling is not standard dental practice) and clamped his jaws tightly together. As you will understand, a whale's mouth cannot forcibly be opened as with a domestic dog.

Peter handed the drill to Bruce. Yes, that was fine. Tanouk would let his friend introduce the spinning drill into the hole in the tooth. The toothy jaws gaped obligingly. The drill buzzed in the trainer's fingers. Bruce gestured for Peter to take over. The Mayfair dental surgeon put out a hand. Tanouk saw the switch. How was he to know that Peter is a top-notch, fashionable dentist from London's West End? His mouth slammed shut with a firm thud. He swam off. No entente cordiale as far as this once Icelandic, but now French, whale was concerned. To my surprise John fared no better when he tried. As for me, Tanouk wouldn't consider even parting his lips for the faintest mocking grin when I mounted the platform.

As the morning wore on, with the whale being left to his own devices from time to time to see if he would relent, Tanouk's resolve merely hardened. There was only one killer whale dentist in the world – Bruce Walton, the whale trainer, the Englishman from Brighton, was the anointed one. 'Very like a whale,' said John, quoting Polonius and shaking his head. We all withdrew for a conference. The conclusion was quickly reached and unanimous. Bruce would have to become the instant dental surgeon, the first person in the history to drill out the pulp cavity of a killer whale's tooth. Peter would be his assistant. I would assist the assistant's assistant, Samantha.

Bruce embarked at once on an ultra-crash course in dental drilling, which bits to use, how and when. Peter instructed him in the way to deal with the conical pulp cavity using the fearsome bit heads – the cylindrical, the club-shaped – when to drill high-speed, when to drill low-speed. Tanouk peeped over the side of his pool as we talked. I fancied he was listening in wry amusement.

So it came to pass that Bruce was left to get on with the job of preparing Tanouk's tooth. We returned, on Bruce's advice, to the restaurant, firstly to reassure Tanouk that we had indeed cleared off and, secondly, to while away the time over the Marineland's excellent lunch of coquilles St Jacques and Bandol wine. Bruce, unlunched, began his surgery. It took him three hours to complete the drilling-out of the cavity which Peter on inspection pronounced 'amazingly perfect'. You know how it is when your dentist stops drilling and begins filling; you start to relax. It was the same for Tanouk. With the humming instruments removed and Bruce in constant attendance, the whale kindly permitted Peter to commence the root treatment and filling process, Samantha handing him one substance after another.

The Blu-Tack waterproofing in between bouts of treatment worked well and the fast-drying chemicals injected into the tooth after the cavity had been sterilized, gradually filled it up and set solid. Peter calculated he used about thirty times more of his special materials than he would have done on the average human incisor.

When the lump of Blu-Tack was removed for the last time, with the root filling iron-hard and level with the rim of the cavity, Tanouk's tooth was safe from the risk of root, or worse, jawbone infection. The whale sprayed half a gallon of water on Peter's green operating suit as he finally closed his great mouth. Dripping wet, Peter and Bruce shook hands.

'You two should form a partnership,' I said. 'Kertesz and Walton – odontologists to the odontocetes.'*

Christine and I stayed on in Antibes for a day or two longer. One of the female killer whales, Sharkan, was due to give birth and I would have loved to be present when parturition commenced. Michael thought I'd be lucky as it was full moon and he had an inkling that the baby whale would arrive under its pale glow. Some sea creatures,

---

* Odontocetes: the sub-order of toothed whales to which killer whales, sperm whales and all dolphins belong.

certain shellfish in particular, are known to be influenced by the phases of the moon. It was not to be, however I'm glad to report that Sharkan gave birth to a healthy baby later on that month.